BIOLOGICAL EVIDENCE

Ann Bucholtz, MD
Jon Lewis, MA

LawTech
Custom Publishing

LawTech Custom Publishing Co., Inc.

(949)498-4815   Fax: (949)498-4858

e-mail: info@LawTechCustomPublishing.com

www.LawTechCustomPublishing.com

Comments and suggestions are welcome.

v. 04.18.07

pp. 317

ISBN: 1-889315-35-4

Contents at a Glance

Table of Articles and Figures

Contents

Chapter 1

Overview of Forensic Science

CHAPTER OVERVIEW

Forensic science is the application of science to the law. Physical evidence has the potential to play a critical role in the resolution of a suspected criminal act. This objective is furthered by the thoughtful, objective and thorough approach to the investigative process. The foundation of forensic science is the preservation of physical evidence that will provide reliable information to aid in an investigation.

In order to appreciate the importance of forensic science, the basic principles must be understood. These principles include proper identification and collection of evidence at a crime scene; knowledge of the best practices in the field of criminalistics; the importance of biological evidence, firearms, documents, toolmarks, impressions, trace evidence and crime scene management. Proper crime scene management includes identification, evaluation, collection and preservation of evidence, thorough search practices, and protection of the scene.

CHAPTER OBJECTIVES

After studying this chapter, the student will be able to:
1. Understand the historical origins of forensic science.
2. Identify advances in forensic science.
3. Identify the major branches of forensic science.

A HISTORICAL PERSPECTIVE

The origins of forensic science can be traced to the 1800s. During this era, forensic specialists were self-taught. There were no special schools, courses or formal training. One of the first significant applications of forensic science occurred in 1888 in London, England. During the late 1880s, "Jack the Ripper" had committed several serial murders. Doctors were allowed to examine his victims for wound patterns.

The use of fingerprint evidence in solving crimes today seems routine and unremarkable. During the 1800s however, fingerprints were the subject of intense scientific research. During the 1880s it was discovered that fingerprints are unique to an individual and remain unchanged over a lifetime. This discovery led to the identification of offenders in criminal investigations.

The Points of Comparison Method

At one time around 1900, there was a system called the anthropometric system that had been invented by Frenchman Alphonse Bertillon (1853-1914), consisting of numerous, minute body measurements, such as finger and forearm lengths. This system was in competition with fingerprinting (technically called dactylography), discovered by Henry Faulds and popularized by Francis Galton. Bertillon based his system on the use of 11 points of comparison, calculating his odds of being wrong on any given match being 4 million to 1. These types of calculations form the basis of a number of forensic sciences relying upon the Points of Comparison method, such as odontology, firearms examination, and questioned document examination. Due to population growth since Bertillon's time, the contemporary method is based on at least 12 points of comparison and an odds ratio of about 6 million to 1. An odds ratio or percent chance of being wrong also characterizes the quantitative information provided by modern analytical techniques such as spectrography, chromatography, and DNA typing (in the case of DNA, the odds ratio is an amazing 30 billion to 1).[1]

During the 1900s forensic science developed into a formal academic discipline. One of the first steps in this progression was the establishment of a forensic science curriculum in 1902 by Swiss Professor R. A. Reiss at the University of Lausanne, Switzerland. This led to the formation of university courses and degrees in criminalistics and police science during the 1930s. Forensic Science and Criminalistics made significant advances along with the rise in technology during the 1900s. The following are some of these advances:

- Establishment of the popular practice of using the comparison microscope for bullet comparison in the 1920s.
- Development of the absorption-inhibition ABO blood typing technique in 1931.
- Invention of the first interference contrast microscope in 1935 by Dutch physicist Frits Zernike (Received Nobel Prize in 1953).
- Development of the chemiluminescent reagent luminol as a presumptive test for blood.
- Study of voice print identification.
- Invention of the Breathalyzer for field sobriety tests.
- Use of heated headspace sampling technique for collecting arson evidence.
- Development of the scanning electron microscope with electron dispersive X-ray technology.
- Identification of the polymorphic nature of red blood cells.
- Enactment of the Federal Rules of Evidence (1975)
- In 1950, the University of California at Berkley established one of the first academic departments of criminology/criminalistics.
- American Academy of Forensic Science (AAFS) was formed in Chicago.
- Evaluation of the gas chromatrograph and the mass spectrometer for forensic purposes.
- Development of the polymerase chain reaction (PCR) technique for clinical and forensic applications.
- In 1980, the use of DNA to solve a crime and exonerate an innocent suspect.
- In 1987, the introduction of DNA and the challenge of certification, accreditation, standardization and quality control guidelines for both DNA Laboratories and the general forensic community.

Criminalistics

Criminalistics is the professional and scientific discipline dedicated to the recognition, collection, identification, individualization and evaluation of physical evidence and the application of the natural sciences to the matters of law. Criminalistics is based on diverse scientific disciplines. Criminalistics draws upon chemistry, biology, physics and mathematics to relate physical evidence to crime. Criminalistics deals with the examination, comparison and identification of evidence like hairs, fibers, glass, paint and footwear using the application of microscopy, chemical and instrumental analysis.

Pathology / Anthropology

Forensic Anthropology is the application of the science of physical anthropology to identify remains. The skeleton can provide evidence of the subject's gender, age when the death occurred, stature, the cause of death and how long the remains have been in their current state. The application of scientific techniques developed in physical anthropology can assist in the investigation of crimes and the discovery of evidence of foul play. Forensic anthropologists work with other forensic science professionals such as forensic pathologists, forensic dentists and law enforcement investigators.

Pathology is the branch of medicine that studies the structural changes to the human body caused by disease or injury. There are two main categories of pathology; anatomical and clinical. Anatomic pathology refers to the study of structural alterations of the human body. Clinical pathology deals with laboratory examination of samples taken from the body. Forensic pathology is a specialization of anatomic pathology. Forensic pathologists perform autopsies to determine the cause and manner of death. A forensic pathologist is an expert in estimating the time of death, the cause of death, the type of weapon used, whether the death was a homicide or suicide and the identification of disease. The forensic pathologist will classify an individual death as homicide, suicide, natural, accidental or undetermined.

Chemistry / Serology

Forensic Chemistry is analytical chemistry applied to crime scene analysis. Some applications of forensic chemistry would generally include various types of chemical residue analysis. An example would be at the scene of a bomb explosion. A forensic chemist would conduct an analysis of the bomb fragments.

Forensic Serology involves the determination of the type and characteristics of blood, blood testing and bloodstain examination. Forensic Serologists may also analyze semen, saliva, other body fluids and may or may not be involved with DNA typing

Toxicology

The Society of Forensic Toxicologists separates toxicology into three categories: post mortem, human-performance and urine drug testing toxicology. Each of these categories has practical application in the field of forensic science. A toxicological examination may show the presence of alcohol, other types of drugs or poison in the body.

Post-Mortem Forensic Toxicology determines the absence or presence of drugs and their metabolites (volatile chemicals such as ethanol, gases such as carbon monoxide, metals and other toxic chemicals) in human fluids and tissues, and evaluates their role as a determinant or contributory factor in the cause and manner of death.

Human-Performance Forensic Toxicology determines the absence or presence of ethanol and other drugs and chemicals in blood, breath or other appropriate specimen(s), and evaluates their role in modifying human performance or behavior.

Forensic Urine Drug Testing determines the absence or presence of drugs and their metabolites in urine to demonstrate prior use or abuse.[2]

Questioned Documents

A questioned or forensic document is any object onto which a writing or printing has been placed and an issue has developed about its authenticity. Who wrote or placed the writing or printing on the object, or other similar legal questions that arise, are issues that cause the examiner to become involved. Occasionally, the field is referred to as "Handwriting Identification" but this definition is a limited one because a document can be defined as anything that bears marks, signs or symbols having a meaning, or that conveys a message to someone. While both terms can be used interchangeably, the recent term "forensic" shall be used over the older term "questioned document" examination.

There are various specific areas of analysis. Questioned and known handwritten or hand printed documents can be compared to identify the author. Mechanically produced documents can be analyzed to identify the source of the documents. Documents can be examined for erasures, alterations, obliterations, indented writing, secret or disappearing ink. Original texts may also be recovered. Charred and water soaked documents may be examined to recover the original text. Physical matches can be made form the analysis of torn or cut paper products. Items involved in these analyses include: dye diffusion, laser printing, xerography, thermal transfer, authenticity of currency, stamps, passports and other legal papers, typewriters, printers, photocopies, alterations, additions, obliterations and the dating of a document paper, ink or writing.

The following categories represent the major areas of expertise of forensic document examiners. These areas are not rigidly limited; there will always be overlap and evolution.

- Questioned Document Examination. A document examiner analyzes any questioned document and questions of authorship or authenticity may be answered.

- Historical Dating. This area of expertise involves the verification of age and worth of a document or object done by a document examiner. This type of analysis may use Carbon-14 dating.

- Fraud Investigations. This is work that often overlaps with that of the document examiner. It focuses on following the money trail and criminal intent.

- Paper & Ink Specialists. These are public or private experts, who date, type, source, and/or catalogue various types of paper, watermarks, ink, printing/copy/fax machines and computer cartridges using chemical methods.

- Forgery Specialists. These are public or private experts who analyze altered, obliterated, changed or doctored documents and photos using infrared lighting, expensive spectrography equipment or digital enhancement techniques.

- Typewriting Analysts. These are experts on the origin, make and model used in typewritten material.

- Photocopy & LaserJet Specialists. These individuals examine photocopies and LaserJet originated documents to determine the source of the document printing.

- Computer Crime Investigators. This is an emerging group that relates to questioned document examination through some common investigative and testimonial procedures.

Odontology

Odontology is also referred to as forensic dentistry. Dr. Robert B.J. Dorion, a Canadian Forensic Dentist, defines this discipline as follows: "Forensic dentistry, or forensic odontology, is the application of dental and paradental knowledge to the solution of legal issues in civil and in criminal matters. Identification of the living or the deceased, bite mark identification, analysis and comparison, lip print identification, analysis and comparison, rugae print identification, analysis and comparison, patterned injury identification, analysis, comparison, identification of dental specimens at crime scene or elsewhere and evaluation of oro-facial trauma." The means of identification on forensic odontology are teeth, bone, presence of foreign bodies, sinus configuration, skull sutures, soft tissue features, photographic comparisons and DNA.[3]

Engineering

Forensic Engineering involves the examination and identification of materials and metals as well as equipment failures. Forensic engineers reconstruct or re-enact motor vehicle accidents, industrial accidents and fire and explosion incidents. Engineers may provide technical answers to the causes of these types of incidents.

Firearms

Firearms evidence is evidence relating to the discharge of a firearm. Firearms evidence is one of the most common types to be encountered at crime scenes. Firearms evidence includes projectiles, expended cartridge cases, projectile damage, gunshot residues and penetrating projectile wounds.

In the late 18th century, rifled weapons replaced smoothbore pistols and muskets. The rifling caused spent bullets to acquire a distinct signature. Rifling is the process of making grooves in the barrel of rifles to increase the accuracy of the projectile. When the weapon is fired, marks are left on the softer metal bullet as it spins through the barrel. The rifling of an individual weapon is unique due to wear from use. This wear causes the bullet fired from a specific weapon to bear the same distinct markings. When bullets began to be encased in cartridges, even more marks were made, assisting investigators to make a match between a bullet and a gun.

The process of firearms identification relating to matching bullets to guns originated in England during the year of 1835. A bullet was taken from a victim and compared to a bullet mold found in the suspect's home. The bullet and mold were compared and were found to be consistent. When confronted with this finding, the suspect confessed. This is not a precise method of matching; however, it was a start in the area of firearms identification.

In 1902, an expert first proved in a courtroom that a specific gun was used to commit a murder. In America, Oliver Wendell Holmes had read a book about firearms identification and called a gunsmith to test fire the alleged murder weapon into a wad of cotton wool. Holmes then used a magnifying glass to match marks on the bullet from the victim to the test-fired bullet and showed these finding to the jury.

Toolmarks

Toolmarks are frequently encountered in burglary cases; however, they made be found in other types of crimes. They can be found at the scene of violent crimes as well. A situation where a tool, like a wrench, was used as a weapon is an example. Toolmarks may be found where the suspect missed the victim and left evidence of the blow on a wall or other inanimate object.

Toolmarks are impressions produced by a tool or instrument on a receptive surface. Tools are used to break into locked buildings or to open safe doors. Toolmark impressions are also microscopic in nature and are the result of imperfections on the cutting surface of the tool. These marks are the "signature" or identifying characteristics of a specific tool. A microscopic comparison of the toolmarks left at a crime scene and test impressions produced by the suspect tool allow the examiner to identify the tool used in a crime.

Toolmark evidence consists of striations or impressions left by tools on objects at the crime scene and various types of tools found in the possession of suspects. It is possible by means of physical or other comparisons to prove that parts of tools left at a crime scene were broken from damaged tools found in the possession of suspects. In many cases, it is possible to identify the specific tool that made the questioned marks by means of laboratory comparison of the tool and marked objects. In some circumstances, it is also possible to prove that objects they contacted at the crime scene produced marks of various types on tools. Photographs of toolmarks at a scene are useful to document their location but have limited value in their identification. Photography of the microscopic comparison is extremely important for documentation purposes.

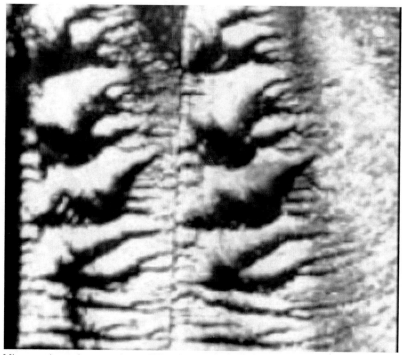

Microscopic tool comparison. This shows the matching groove comparisons. The comparison is made by taking a suspect tool and duplicating its imprint on a similar piece of material (door jam) collected as scene evidence. The two impressions are compared side-by-side under the comparison microscope.

The examination of tools and evidence with toolmarks is based upon microscopically observable class and individual characteristics. Pliers and screwdrivers for example, can be eliminated as having produced certain toolmarks if those impressions are significantly larger or smaller than the width of the tools' grasping jaws or blades. The distance between a toothed instrument's teeth is considered a class characteristic. Individual characteristics, produced during the manufacture and use of the tool are unique to that particular tool or toolmark. Individual characteristics also include noticeable defects such as missing or partial teeth, raised metal nodes or ridges, distinctive signs of wear or damage, or a broken tip or blade.

The results of the examination of toolmarks fall into three categories; identification, elimination and no conclusion. Identification signifies a match between two toolmarks or a match between a tool and evidence with toolmarks. An exclusion or non-identification denotes a lack of association between two items of evidence. The possibility that a specific tool produced a given mark is excluded. No conclusion indicates sufficient corresponding evidence characteristics are not present. The examiner is consequently unable to classify the evidence as an identification or exclusion.

Fingerprints

Fingerprints, palm prints and footprints are among the most important pieces of evidence to be gathered. They display individual characteristics, which can be traced to only one person. This type of direct evidence is important. It places an individual at a scene where a print was lifted. Fingerprints are a deposit of body oils, water and salts that are left behind after a suspect touches a printable object. They display the pattern of friction ridges that all people have on the pads of their fingers. These are specific to each individual (no two persons can have the exact same fingerprint patterns). In short, the investigator can easily make or break the investigation based on the effort that is invested in the gathering of latent prints.

There are three basic fingerprint patterns. These patterns are loops, arches and whorls. Each of these patterns is comprised of minutiae points. There are thirty different types of minutiae points found in fingerprints. There are no two people who have the same types of minutiae, in the same number, in the same places on their fingertips. This is what makes each individual's fingerprints unique.

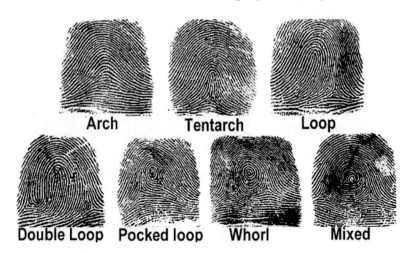

Arch   Tentarch   Loop

Double Loop   Pocked loop   Whorl   Mixed

Contaminated and latent prints are different types of fingerprints. Contaminated fingerprints are prints that have been contaminated by other material such as ink, pigments, oils, paint, blood, flour and grease. Latent fingerprints are the "average" prints found at most scenes. These prints are left behind as the result of deposits of small amounts of bodily oil and sweat. The oil itself is usually picked up on the fingers from other parts of the body. The pads of the fingers themselves do not contain oil glands.

Latent fingerprints are normally developed through the application of a powder. This powder is used specifically for the purpose of collecting prints. Powders are available in a number of colors; however, black is the most common. The powder is applied to the surface with a brush made from fiberglass, camel's hair, feather or nylon. The powder adheres to the latent finger ridge patterns left by the individual. The print is then covered with a clear tape, lifted from the surface, and applied to a glossy paper card. The card is submitted to identification specialists for analysis.

Fingerprints can be lifted from paper. Recently applied latent prints can be lifted from glossy paper such as photographs. Older latent fingerprints will fade after a period of time due to the absorption of the oil by the paper. In these cases, the print may still be developed by the use of iodine development. The equipment used in this process is quite bulky; therefore, this process is normally conducted in the laboratory. Fingerprints may also be lifted from dead bodies. There are methods than can be used by trained laboratory personnel to develop latent prints from homicide victims.

Fingerprints are recorded and preserved on the original cards used at the scene during collection. Fingerprints are also recorded by photographs, particularly in the case where a print is visible without the use of development powder. Computer imaging of fingerprints is also becoming increasingly common.

Jurisprudence

The Fourth Amendment of the Constitution provides each of us the right to be free from "unreasonable" searches of our persons, houses and property. "The right of the people to be secure in their persons, houses, papers and effects, against unreasonable searches and seizures, shall not be violated, and no warrants shall issue, but upon probable cause, supported by oath or affirmation, and particularly describing the place to be searched, and the persons or things to be seized." A "search" occurs when the government or its agents have infringed on a legitimate, reasonable expectation of privacy. A "seizure" of property occurs when there has been a meaningful infringement of an individual's possession of that property. A "seizure" of a person occurs under two circumstances; when a peace officer applies force or when a person voluntarily submits to the peace officer's authority.

The "Exclusionary Rule" does not appear anywhere in the Constitution, it was created by the Supreme Court in a case decision to encourage proper government conduct. The legality of a search or seizure may be challenged prior to a criminal case going to trial. A pre-trial "suppression" motion may be made. In this hearing, the court will make the determination as to whether or not the search or seizure in question was lawful. If the court finds the search or seizure to be "unreasonable" then the evidence gathered as a result will be "excluded" from the trial, hence the "Exclusionary Rule." This exclusion of evidence serves as a penalty for the illegality of the search or seizure.

The legal aspects of forensic science are extremely important. In terms of biological evidence, a search warrant may be necessary to obtain certain personal identifying characteristics such as finger and palm prints, blood samples, saliva samples, urine samples and photographs. Criminal cases are won and lost every day based upon search and seizure issues. There are volumes of case decisions that deal specifically with this area of law. The best science and experts available cannot help a case when important evidence has been excluded as the result of an unconstitutional search or seizure.

There are three landmark cases in the area of forensic science. These cases are Frye v. United States, People v. Kelly and Daubert v. Merrell Dow Pharmaceuticals. In 1932, Frye v. United States was a federal court decision regarding the expert opinion testimony on new scientific procedures. In this case, the defendant attempted to show his innocence by introducing the results of a lie detector test. This test, according to the defendant, showed that he was telling the truth and did not kill the victim. The court ruled that this evidence was inadmissible because the scientific principles on which the test relied were not "sufficiently established to have gained general acceptance in the particular field in which it belongs." This decision established the "Frye" general acceptance test.

In People v. Kelly, the Supreme Court of California expanded on the Frye decision. The Court found the Frye standard to be protective in nature. The protective aspect is that it shields jurors from being overly influenced by the impressive nature of scientific based testimony. It also protects the rights of criminal defendants that are in the position of new science being used to convict them of crimes and it protects California common law from precedents that would allow the introduction of evidence based upon questionable scientific grounds. The Kelly / Frye Standard requires "a preliminary showing of general acceptance of the new technique in the relevant scientific community."

In 1975, the United States Supreme Court addressed the question of whether or not the Frye Standard would continue to be the admissibility standard for expert testimony. In Daubert v. Merrell Dow Pharmaceuticals, a new standard was developed to instruct judges. To determine reliability and relevance of testimony the court must conduct a "preliminary assessment of whether the reasoning or methodology underlying the testimony is scientifically valid and whether that reasoning or methodology can properly be applied to the facts at issue."[4]

These decisions were designed to keep "junk science" out of the courtroom. The courts will allow only scientific evidence and expert testimony that is based in proven, accepted scientific analysis.

CAREERS IN FORENSIC SCIENCE

Forensic sciences are professions that assist criminal and civil investigations and the judicial system through science. The following areas are recognized career paths within the forensic science field:

Criminalists
- Study physical and biologic evidence for these purposes
- Have bachelor's degrees with strong natural science cores or degrees
- There are crime scene technicians who respond to scenes, photograph and retrieve evidence. These qualifications include associates and bachelor degrees.

Forensic Pathologists
- Are medical doctors (bachelor & medical school degrees, 4 to 5 yrs of residency and fellowship in forensic pathology)
- Purpose is to determine cause and manner of death through autopsies and death investigation

Forensic Psychiatrists
- Are medical doctors (bachelor & medical school degrees, 4 yr psychiatry residency and training in forensic psychiatry)
- Serve the judicial system in mental competency exams, criminal and legal proceedings

Forensic Anthropologists
- Have bachelor's degree in physical anthropology with graduate degrees in forensic or physical anthropology
- Study skeletal remains and assist with evaluation of skeletal trauma and identification of unknown remains

Forensic Odontologists
- Are dentists (bachelor and dental school degrees, specialty interest in forensic identification)
- Study dental issues include bite marks and dental identification of unknown or severely traumatized remains

Forensic Entomologists
- Have their doctorates in entomology (bugs and insects)
- Aid investigations by studying insects found at crime scenes and on bodies to assist with reconstruction of the time or circumstances of death

Forensic Engineers
- Specialize in physics, chemistry, geophysics, etc., and often have doctorate degrees.
- Function in accident reconstruction and product liability investigations

Forensic Toxicologists
- Have bachelor, masters or doctorate degrees in chemistry or pharmacology
- Assist investigations by providing data regarding levels of drugs in body fluids, identification of drug substances.

SOURCES

"Education and Training in Forensic Science"
- http://www.ncjrs.org/pdffiles1/nij/203099.pdf

"Choosing a career in Forensic Science"
- http://www.aafs.org/default.asp?section_id=resources&page_id=choosing_a_career
- http://www.aafs.org/default.asp?section_id=resources&page_id=colleges_and_universities

SUMMARY

Forensic science has advanced over the years along with technology and science from basic fingerprint identification to complex DNA analysis. Each branch of science can contribute to the investigation of crimes. Each new advance in forensic science can help make investigations more thorough and accurate.

DISCUSSION QUESTIONS

1. What is "the points of comparison method"?
2. Pick a branch of forensic science and provide an example of a situation in which it may be applied.
3. Explain the "Exclusionary Rule."

ADDITIONAL READINGS

Handbook of Forensic Services, Lawtech Custom Publishing
Advancing Justice through DNA Technology, Office of the President, http://www.ojp.usdoj.gov March 2003
Crime Scene Investigation Guide, Lawtech Custom Publishing

ENDNOTES

1. *An Introduction to Criminalistics and Physical Evidence*; Tom O'Connor PhD, North Carolina Wesleyan University (http://faculty.ncwc.edu.)
2. Society of Forensic Toxicologists www.soft.org
3. ca.geocities.com/dorionforensic/dentistry.htm.
4. *From Frye to Daubert;* Daniel S. Fridman and J. Scott Janoe Berkman Center for Internet and Society and Harvard Law School, http://cyber.law.harvard.edu/daubert/about.htm.

Chapter 2

The Crime Scene

CHAPTER OVERVIEW

At any crime scene, investigators have "one shot" to collect and process evidence. Over time, potential evidence may be destroyed or become contaminated. In order to facilitate thorough evidence collection, the scene must be secured and searched properly. The chain of custody begins at the crime scene with accurate documentation.

OBJECTIVES

After studying this chapter, the student will be able to:

1. Understand the factors involved in securing and processing a crime scene.
2. Identify the types of systematic crime scene searches.
3. Understand the importance of thorough crime scene documentation.

SECURING THE SCENE

When approaching a scene, the goal to keep in mind is to contain the scene with as little contamination or disturbance of physical evidence as possible.

The first step in this process is to secure the area. There may be people gathered, potential witnesses, onlookers etc. First responders must stabilize the area while being observant of any people, vehicles or other potential evidence. Depending on the number of people to be identified and interviewed, additional resources may be necessary. For example, at the scene of a bank robbery, there would be a number of people present that need to be identified. It is not practical for one person to perform this task as well as processing the scene for physical evidence. In this situation, it may be wise to separate these witnesses to different parts of the bank, or perhaps outside. This protects the scene from potential contamination and facilitates independent interviews of these people.

Perimeter Establishment

A perimeter is part of securing the scene. The general rule when establishing a perimeter around a scene is to start with a large area and then tighten boundaries if possible. When establishing a perimeter "bigger is better." It is much more difficult to expand a perimeter once it has been established. The basic goal of a perimeter is to secure and protect potential evidence. It also defines the crime scene for purposes of searching, documenting and collecting of evidence.

The first responders to any scene are responsible for setting the perimeter. The perimeter should be established based on the focal point of the scene. Factors to be considered in the establishment of a crime scene perimeter are: where the crime occurred, places where the victim/evidence may have been moved, and points of entry and exit. Physical barriers should be used to define the perimeter. The most common means is the use of yellow plastic tape with the words "Crime Scene Do Not Enter" or something to that effect written in black letters. Ropes, cones, vehicles or existing physical barriers can be used. Care should be taken, particularly with outdoor scenes to insure protection from the elements (wind, rain, snow).

Once the perimeter is set, personnel must be deployed to maintain its integrity. This includes a written log of each person to enter the scene (time in, time out and purpose), controlling and restricting access to authorized people, and controlling the activity of these people once inside. It is not appropriate to smoke or use tobacco while inside a scene, use the phone, use the bathroom, change the thermostat or otherwise move objects unnecessarily. These actions are not only unprofessional; they have the potential to destroy potential evidence.

Once the scene has been secured and protected, control may be turned over to the lead investigator and criminalist. The first responders are required to give a briefing of actions and observations made to the investigator. Once the investigator assumes control, first responders typically remain at the scene in a support role. This role typically involves the maintenance of the perimeter, controlling the scene and briefing the next in command of the initial aspects of the scene prior to subsequent investigation. In all cases, first responders are to remain at the scene until formally relieved of their responsibilities.

Safety Issues

Handling biological evidence can be very dangerous. The dangers of blood borne pathogens such as Hepatitis B and HIV are well documented. When processing a scene, the safest approach is to treat all biological materials as hazardous. Personal Protective Equipment (PPE) should be worn to protect and shield from the biological hazards that may be encountered at a crime scene. Basic PPE include gloves, boots, coveralls and other over garments. There are some scenes, such as a clandestine drug lab, that may require the use of respiratory equipment and encapsulated suits.

Protecting Biological Evidence

The first part of the collection process is the identification of biological evidence that will allow for serology and/or DNA testing. Always use proper safety equipment to prevent contact with hazardous materials. Evidence should be protected from contamination. This is facilitated by the proper collection, packaging and storage of biological evidence. All evidence must be documented and labeled to maintain the chain of custody.

DNA and serology testing can be conducted on biological materials depending on the quantity and condition of the evidence submitted. Biological materials than can be tested include, whole blood and blood stains, semen and vaginal fluid, soft tissues and organs, hairs with a root, saliva, bones, teeth and nails, products of conception, urine, fresh fecal samples, skin cells from clothing, ear wax, mucus and fresh vomitus material. When collecting a sample, the best procedure is to collect the object with the stain rather than removing the stain from the object. If biological evidence is not properly collected and packaged, DNA has a potential for degradation. Paper is the best material for packing because paper is porous and allows for air exchange with the atmosphere. Paper bags and envelopes work well. Do not use plastic. Improper packaging may also result in cross contamination. All items of evidence should be packaged separately.

CRIME SCENE SEARCH

First responders to a crime scene will many times encounter a situation of mass confusion and disorder. The search for evidence however, must be disciplined and thorough. It is important to have a plan to search the scene. This will facilitate the covering of all areas to be searched in a methodical and systematical fashion. Follow a plan; never search on intuition or by meandering about the scene. Search methodically and limit the number of people searching to as few as reasonably necessary.

When conducting a search designate as "finder" and "recorder." The "finder" is the primary set of eyes and does the majority of the physical searching. The "recorder" works in concert with the "finder" and documents items of evidence discovered during the search.

There are a variety of search methods, depending upon the type of evidence, location, available personnel and resources, and time constraints. Some of the more common types of searches include a concentric search, a strip search, a grid search, a zone search, a clockwise-counter clockwise search, and a pie pattern. A *concentric* or *spiral* search follows a circular pattern from outside in or inside out. It's useful if resources are limited, the area is relatively open, and the search is for large items, such as a body, gun, safe, etc. In a *strip* search or lane search, an area is divided into parallel strips. Each area is searched before moving to the next area. It's helpful when teams are looking for just about anything. Stakes and twine are used to identify the teams specific search lanes. In a *grid* search the area is divided into north-south and east-west strips, allowing a secondary search of each area from a different direction. It's useful when teams are used to search a large area for hard to find items. In a *zone* or *sector* search the area in question, usually a room, is divided into equal size zones. A searcher is assigned to each zone and is used mostly for trace evidence searches. A specific search pattern is used in each zone. The *clockwise – counter clockwise* inside search pattern involves two people working together. One person searches in a clockwise direction searching the area from the waist up to the ceiling. The second person searches counter clockwise waist down to floor. When one pass is completed the searchers reverse roles and repeat the process. A *pie* or *wheel* pattern is used with four people looking for trace evidence. This is similar to the zone search, but not illustrated here.

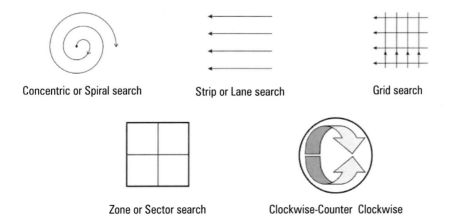

Concentric or Spiral search   Strip or Lane search   Grid search

Zone or Sector search   Clockwise-Counter Clockwise

SCENE DOCUMENTATION (NOTES, SKETCH, PHOTOS, VIDEO)

The proper documentation of a crime scene is critical. This documentation must be thorough and detailed. It is important to include as many details as possible. Often times a small detail like whether or not the lights were on at a scene during the initial response can become important in the subsequent investigation. Factors to be considered in the documentation of a scene include: conditions upon arrival (lights on/off, doors open/closed, smells, weather, temperature, etc.) observations of the scene including the location of persons and items as well as their condition, identification of witnesses, victims and suspects, and any actions taken (forced entry by officers, medical treatment by emergency medical personnel).

Note Taking

Note taking is critical for accurate documentation of a scene. Notes should follow a chronological order and be clearly and legibly written. Notes must be specific, avoiding general terms like "near." Specific measurements should be used instead. These notes can be subpoenaed in court and will be judged on their appearance and content. Many officers at the scene of an investigation use tape recorders and the later transcribe the contents to an official report.

A common way of documenting a crime scene is the use of pre-printed forms. Law enforcement agencies have forms for use at scenes to record all aspects of the investigation. These forms are constantly under revision and kept current based upon trial and error experiences on actual cases. These forms may vary in length and appearance from agency to agency; however, the objective is still the same. These forms are drafted for routine use and are generic by design. The important thing to remember when using these forms is that they are designed to be a general guideline, not an exhaustive list of possibilities to cover at a scene. They are reminders of the minimum information required in investigating a scene. Each scene will be individualized and requires specific documentation. There are no two scenes that are the same. Forms are to aid, remind, and are by no means a substitute for thinking, training and experience.

Photography

The purpose of photographing is to create a visual record of the scene and the evidence collected. Each view (overall, medium and close range) has a separate purpose. Overall views are taken to show the largest view of the scene possible. Mid-range views depict the relationship between items. Close range views document the items of evidence individually including serial numbers, tags or other details.

When photographs are being used in the analytical process, photos of stationary objects should be taken using a tripod with the proper lighting techniques to create any needed shadows. A second photo adding a measuring device (a ruler) should be taken of the same item.

The following are the basic steps followed by crime scene photographers:
- Photograph the entire area before it is entered.
- Photograph victims, the crowd and vehicles in the area.
- Photograph the entire scene including the three views, overall, medium and close range. Use a measuring device when appropriate.
- Take photos of items of evidence before they are moved or handled. Coordinate this effort with personnel at the scene (sketch preparer, evidence recorder and evidence recovery personnel).
- Photograph all latent fingerprints and other impression evidence (shoe prints, tire tracks) before they are lifted or cast.
- Complete the photographic log and a photographic sketch.

Diagram or Sketch

The diagram or sketch records the location of physical evidence as well as their relationship to other objects at the scene. The sketch includes measurements of the sizes of objects and distances between them. Sketches are used in combination with written reports and photos to document a scene. The sketch is simply a drawing of the crime scene.

The sketch is drawn to show the size and distance relationships between items at a scene. The drawing does not have to be to scale, however, must include exact measurements. Sketches are important because they can cover a large area and be drawn to leave out unnecessary clutter (unlike photographs).

The following are the basic steps involved in the completion of a crime scene sketch:

- Diagram the immediate area.
- Detail the major items of evidence.
- Label the areas to be searched and coordinate these labels with the crime scene team leader (i.e. room number one, office, living room, etc).
- Take necessary measurements. Always double-check your measurements.
- Include any administrative information or disclaimers such as "not to scale."

EVIDENCE COLLECTION

Physical evidence is collected for the purpose of comparison with other items or materials. In order to facilitate comparison, certain considerations must be addressed. First, a sufficient sample of the evidence to be compared should be collected. The amount of specimen to gather is largely a function of experience. A general rule is to collect as much material as reasonably possible. It is better to gather too much material, than not enough.

Known or control samples must be collected. If a bloodstained shirt is submitted for analysis, there must be something to compare it to. Items for comparison may be samples of the victim's blood and the suspect's blood. In traffic collision investigations, paint transfer collected from the victim's vehicle may be compared with a known sample from the suspect's vehicle.

Blank samples may also be required for analysis. In an event involving bloodstained carpet, a segment of the unstained carpet must be collected from the area next to the stain. This blank or control sample is necessary for testing to determine that the sample alone does not interfere with or influence the analysis. It serves as a baseline of data contributed by the carpet alone. This helps to prevent a false positive result and incorrect conclusions.

Suspect, control and blank samples are never to be packaged together. Individual packaging will prevent contamination or cross contamination.

Evidence Preservation Overview

Evidence at a crime scene may come in a variety of forms. Due to the diverse nature of physical evidence, basic procedures have been developed to collect these items safely. Law enforcement agencies and crime labs have standard operating procedures for marking and packaging evidence. These procedures are based upon safety concerns, maintaining evidence integrity and chain of custody.

Firearms

Firearms and other weapons are by definition dangerous items to handle. An unloaded firearm is marked with a tag attached to a string. The string is looped through the trigger guard of the firearm and sealed with a gummed label around the knot. Tools and knives are marked in the same manner. Once the tool or weapon has been marked, it is placed in an appropriately sized envelope. The envelope is marked and sealed over with a gummed label.

Vials

Pill vials, glass vials and plastic vials are used to package dried blood, dried saliva swabs, and expended shell casings or bullets. These vials are sealed with a gummed label wrapped around the cap and mouth of the vial. The vials are then placed into a labeled envelope.

Large or Over-Sized Items

Some items are just too big to be packaged in the manner described above. These items include tires, televisions or stereos. Items such as these should be labeled with a stringed property tag sealed with a gummed label.

Vehicles

Vehicles seized as evidence should also be labeled. After a vehicle has been processed, a stringed evidence tag should be laced through the steering wheel and sealed. Vehicles are usually stored in an approved impound lot.

Forgery or Paper Evidence

Forgery or "paper" evidence includes documents such as checks, currency and credit cards. These paper items are to be labeled with the officer's name, date and case number, on the back of the document in a manner that does not interfere with the original markings or endorsements. Credit cards are to be marked by placing clear tape on the back of the card, below the signature area, with the required information written on the tape. In the situation where a witness has accepted a document, such as a bank teller accepting a counterfeit check, the witness must initial the item before giving it to the investigating officer. The purpose of this is to aid the witness in identification of the item in later court proceedings.

Chain of Custody

The establishment and maintenance of the chain of custody prevents allegations of evidence tampering, theft, planting or contamination. Proper marking and packaging of evidence is critical in maintaining the chain of custody. The accurate documentation, collection and preservation of items assure integrity of the evidence. A properly maintained chain of evidence will reduce the likelihood of challenges later on in court.

The chain of custody begins with the designation of a custodian of evidence at the scene. In most law enforcement agencies, this person is the first responding forensic specialist or crime scene technician. The custodian of evidence generates and maintains the chain of custody for all evidence collected at the scene. Documentation begins with the location of the scene, and time of arrival. The custodian of evidence determines which personnel are responsible for collection of specific evidence, and the collection priority for fragile or perishable evidence. Each item of evidence should be identified, secured and preserved in the prescribed manner. The collection of evidence is documented to include the location at the scene, time of collection and location of storage. The crime scene log is also established, including the entry and exit of personnel, victims and witnesses.

The goal of the chain of custody is to be able to account for every movement of a specific piece of evidence after collection from the scene. The following is an example of the chain of custody for an item of blood evidence. During a homicide investigation in a residence, blood is found near the front door. The location where the blood was found in relation to the crime scene is documented in writing and sketched. A photograph is taken of the blood. The blood is collected using a swab and packaged in the appropriate vial. The person who collected the blood seals and labels the vial. The vial remains in that person's custody until taken from the scene and secured in a controlled evidence locker at the lab or police facility. This item will be sent to the crime lab for DNA analysis. When this occurs, the person checking it out documents the movement and takes responsibility for the evidence. The links of the chain insure that the evidence can be accounted for at all times, whether at the scene, in the evidence locker or in the crime lab. The ideal chain of evidence is as short as possible and unbroken.

When evidence is collected from a scene, the specific item must be able to be identified as being the same item in court. This can be accomplished in several ways. The most basic means of identification is when an item of evidence has a serial number. The item's serial number should be recorded on reports, property invoices, envelopes and property tags. Some items may have identifying marks. Unique marks like scratches, dents or engraving should be recorded in reports or property invoices. Non-serialized items should be packaged and sealed with the department report number listed on the property invoice.

Most law enforcement agencies have developed forms used specifically for identification of property and evidence. These forms usually contain blank fields which require identifying information be completed. In all cases, the following basic information should be included on all evidence containers, tags and labels:

- The date and time the item was collected, and the location where it was found.
- The agency's case number.
- The location where the evidence was transported to and stored.
- The type of crime.
- Each time the evidence is removed to and from storage.
- The victim's and suspect's name.
- A brief description of the item.
- The name of the person who collected the items.

A simple acronym for first responders covers the basic crime scene responsibilities is:

RESPOND

Respond: Follow proper tactics and techniques when conducting a criminal investigation.

Evaluate: Assess the overall condition of the scene.

<u>S</u>ecure: Secure the scene and protect the evidence.

<u>P</u>rotect: Preserve evidence from loss or contamination.

<u>O</u>bserve: Recognize items or evidence and recover them.

<u>N</u>otify: Request necessary specialists or assistance.

<u>D</u>ocument: Documentation of the entire process to establish "Chain of Custody."

SUMMARY

The thorough processing of a crime scene is important to the overall investigation. This process begins with securing the scene and establishing a perimeter. Once this is accomplished, evidence should be collected in a systematic manner with proper safety precautions. Documentation of this process is critical in maintaining the chain of custody.

DISCUSSION QUESTIONS

1. Why is crime scene documentation important?
2. What are three types of systematic crime scene searches?
3. What is the chain of custody?

ADDITIONAL READING

Brunelle, R. (1982). "Questioned Document Examination" in R. Saferstein (ed.) Forensic Science Handbook. Englewood Cliffs, NJ: Prentice-Hall.

"What Every Law Enforcement Officer Should Know about DNA Evidence." Best Practices for Identification, Preservation and Collection of DNA Evidence at a Crime Scene. www.ojp.usdoj.gov/nij/dna.

Handbook of Forensic Services, United States Department of Justice, Federal Bureau of Investigation: http://www.fbi.gov/hq/lab/handbook/scene1.htm#Preliminary%20Survey & www.fbi.gov 1999.

Crime Scene Investigation, Office of Justice Programs, National Institute of Justice, http://www.ojp.usdoj.gov; http://www.ojp.usdoj.gov/nij, 1999,

California Commission on Peace Officer Standards and Training's workbook for the "Forensic Technology for Law Enforcement" Telecourse presented on May 13, 1993.

California Commission on Peace Officer Standards and Training's workbook for the "Forensic Technology for Law Enforcement" Tele-course presented on May 13, 1993; http://www.crime-scene-investigator.net/respon3.html

Collection of Physical Evidence: Utilization of the Crime Scene Examination Section and Crime Scene Search Officers, Metropolitan Police Department Washington D.C., 1992; http://www.lefande.com/MPDGOs/304.08.htm

Chapter 3

Biological Evidence

OVERVIEW

This chapter defines what evidence is, where we find it and general principles in handling evidence. Also discussed are basic lab methodologies for evaluation of evidence.

CHAPTER OBJECTIVES

After studying this chapter, the student will be able to:
1. Understand what evidence is and how it is deposited at a crime scene.
2. Understand class characteristics and individualizing characteristics for different types of evidence.
3. Understand the process of labeling evidence.
4. Understand the basic principles of laboratory instrumentation.

HISTORICAL PERSPECTIVES

Criminalistics is the scientific profession that collects, identifies and interprets physical and biological evidence. The term criminalistics originated in the late 1800s by Hans Gross, an investigating magistrate for the University of Prague. He described in his book the need for scientifically trained investigators who could assist criminal investigators with the technical and scientific aspects of a crime.

WHAT IS EVIDENCE?

Virtually any object can serve as a piece of evidence (Table 3.1). Evidence is evaluated to link a suspect to a crime, to clear a suspect or to reconstruct a series of events that occurred during the crime. Collection of evidence should be done with one of these three ideas in mind.

There are two major classes of evidence, physical and biological:

1) *Physical evidence* includes all items such as fingerprints, bullets, fibers, glass, soil, paint, documents or toolmarks.

2) *Biological evidence* is a sub-category and includes items such as blood, semen, hair, bones, bodies, urine, and other body fluids, all having their origin in living tissue.

Table 3.1 Possible DNA Evidence Locations and Sources

Evidence	Possible Location of DNA on the Evidence	Source of DNA
Baseball bat or similar weapon	Handle, end	Sweat, skin, blood, tissue
Hat, bandanna or mask	Inside	Sweat, hair, dandruff
Eyeglasses	Nose or ear pieces, lens	Sweat, skin
Facial tissue, cotton swab	Surface area	Mucus, blood, sweat, semen, ear wax
Dirty laundry	Surface area	Blood, sweat, semen
Toothpick	Tips	Saliva
Used cigarette	Cigarette butt	Saliva
Stamp or envelope	Licked area	Saliva
Tape or ligature	Inside/outside surface	Skin, sweat
Bottle, can or glass	Sides, mouthpiece	Saliva, sweat
Used condom	Inside/outside surface	Semen, vaginal or rectal cells
Blanket, pillow, sheet	Surface area	Sweat, hair, semen, urine, saliva
"Through & through" bullet	Outside surface	Blood, tissue
Bite mark	Person's skin or clothing	Saliva
Fingernail, partial fingernail	Scrapings	Blood, sweat, tissue

Source: http://www.ncjrs.org/pdffiles1/nij/bc000614.pdf

WHERE IS EVIDENCE?

Evidence gets deposited in a crime scene by transfer of materials from the offender to the victim. It is stated that whenever two surfaces interact, a transfer of evidence will occur. This is called the Locard Exchange Postulate.[1]

To locate evidence that is not visible with usual means of light and vision (sunlight or ambient light), alternate light sources can be used. Conventional means can be blue light with orange glasses to visualize semen. Advances have been made to now include criminalistics light-imaging units (CLU). These units use various colors of light to view evidence under normal lighting conditions, which is an improvement over conventional alternate light sources, which need darkened rooms or may even need examination at night to view faint evidence images.

Many times the problem isn't that the transfer did not occur but being able to detect it among the myriad of surfaces. After finding material that may be evidence, it can be a judgment call whether it is relevant and how much potential evidence needs to be collected. In some cases some fibers may be the link that cracks a case; in other cases they may be irrelevant. The judgment takes experience and communication with other investigators at the scene for their input. When in doubt, collect it. Facts at the time of the initial investigation are just that, initial facts. Sometimes the case scenario changes with further investigation. It is best to have all the evidence necessary to support or disprove new hypotheses. There is usually only one chance to collect data in its most pristine and best condition. After that, it may be altered or irretrievable.

The next task is to determine the origin of the evidence. The purpose of the lab is to take a piece of evidence and identify its source, referred to as class characteristics. The next task, if possible, is to identify features which make it unique and to narrow the origin of the source to the smallest population possible. These features are called individualizing characteristics. Example: An unknown yellow substance is found on a shirt. Sampling, fluorescence and microscopy reveal nonliving material with class characteristics consistent with wax. The individualizing characteristics are that it is yellow candle wax with components manufactured by a particular company.

Before evidence is collected, the need for a search warrant or court order should be considered. Court orders may be necessary to obtain evidence from a living person (suspect) such as saliva, blood or bite mark impressions. Search warrants may be necessary to seize evidence from certain suspected crime scenes. If either is not met, the evidence may not be admissible in court.

LABELING OF EVIDENCE

Evidence packages should be labeled with the following information using an indelible marker:
- The assigned case number
- Your name or initials
- Date and time of collection
- What is contained in the evidence package
- Location where the evidence was found

Seal the container with evidence tape, initial and date the seal. All evidence should be recorded on an evidence list.

GENERAL PRINCIPLES IN COLLECTION OF EVIDENCE

- Package and handle evidence to minimize potential contamination or cross-transfer
- Change gloves and thoroughly clean implements (e.g., tweezers, razor blades, saws) when collecting samples from different sources
- Use separate containers for individual items
- Use sheets of paper to minimize contact between different surfaces of the same evidence
- Collect loose trace evidence from clothing prior to handling.
- Air-dry clothing if it is damp and store in paper bags. If clothing contains biological evidence, it should be stored frozen.
- Treat all biological samples as infective material. Follow your agency's Bloodborne Pathogen procedure.
- Keep any contaminated surface (e.g., gloved hand) away from face to prevent contact with the eyes, nose or mouth
- After dealing with evidence, properly dispose of gloves and wash hands with germicidal soap
- It may be necessary to collect control samples (known samples from a victim as a standard), reference samples from a scene to determine basic background of the samples so they can be eliminated during the testing, and elimination samples of items that may have contaminated the scene (first responders, people living in a residence, etc).[2]

LABORATORY EQUIPMENT

How is the evidence evaluated? Multiple instruments and personnel are needed to evaluate submitted evidence. Various kinds of equipment form the backbone of a crime laboratory along with skilled criminalists who analyze the instrument data.

Basic chemistry terms need to be discussed briefly. An atom is a basis of matter and is composed of neutrons, protons and electrons. The number of these particles is the differentiation of one atom from another. A molecule is a combination of atoms, for example carbon dioxide (CO_2

is an atom of carbon and two atoms of oxygen) that is the smallest combination of that substance and still retains the same properties. An element is an atom with the same number of protons. A compound is composed of two or more atoms with a fixed ratio. For example, water is composed of hydrogen and oxygen (H_2O) in a ratio of two hydrogen atoms to one oxygen atom.

Microscopes

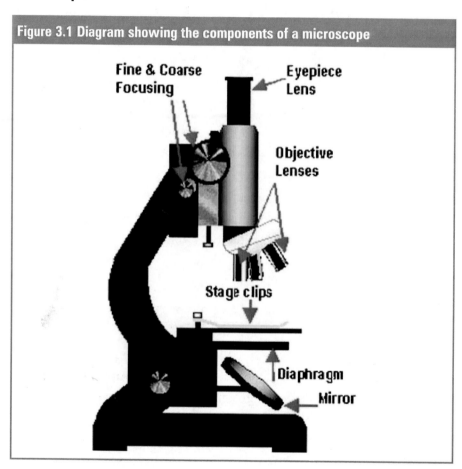

Figure 3.1 Diagram showing the components of a microscope

Source: www.wikipedia.org/wiki/microscopes

Microscopes come in all shapes and sizes. The basic principle is to take an image and magnify it so that it can be seen with greater detail. (Figure 3.1) The method and degree of magnification determines in part what type of function it will perform and what microscopic evidence it can analyze.

Light Microscope

The light microscope is the standard type of microscope most people think of. It magnifies an image through a series of lenses arranged to compound or multiply the magnifying ability of each lens in succession. Most have a built in light source and for ease of operation come with two eyepieces (called a binocular microscope). These microscopes are useful to identify samples of hair, semen, fibers and micro-organisms. Some of them have the ability to polarize the light (filter the beam from the light source so that only parallel light rays are permitted to visualize the specimen). This principle is valuable to look at crystalline material and fibers.

Comparison Microscope

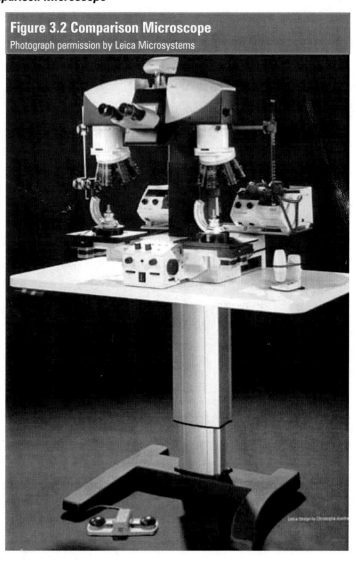

Figure 3.2 Comparison Microscope
Photograph permission by Leica Microsystems

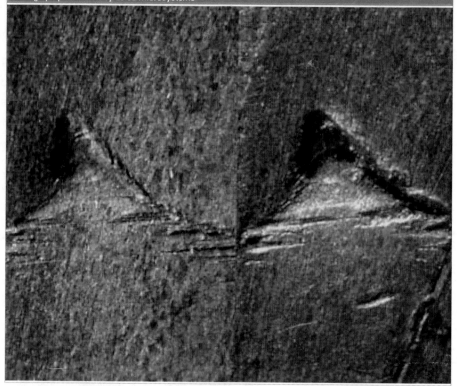

Figure 3.3 Comparison microscope view of two bullet casings showing matching ejector marks.
Photograph permission by Leica Microsystems

A comparison microscope is two light microscopes hooked side by side so that two specimens can be compared simultaneously. There are two stages (platforms where the specimen mounted on a glass slide is placed for visual observation through the microscope), two magnifying systems and a single eyepiece where the two specimens can be visualized side by side in a single split field (Figures 3.2 & 3.3). This is very useful to compare the striations from two bullets, or the ejection marks on two casings for their similarities and in turn matches them to a suspect weapon. A comparison microscope can also be useful in fiber, hair and other trace analysis for simultaneous visualization and comparison of collected evidence to suspect or victim sources.

Scanning Electron Microscope

A scanning electron microscope is like a light microscope in that its purpose is to view an image of some object. The big differences are that it uses an electron beam to illuminate the specimen and it can magnify an object 500,000 times. It is useful to illustrate very small objects and surface details of the evidence. These microscopes are expensive and may only be available at the larger crime labs or at the FBI.

CHROMATOGRAPHY

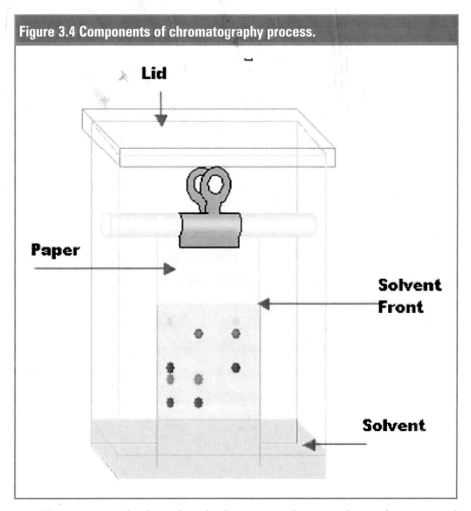

Figure 3.4 Components of chromatography process.

Chromatography is a chemical process where a mixture is separated by being carried in a mobile phase (a liquid or a gas) across a stationary phase (a solid like a gel or paper). The mixture separates by moving along with the mobile phase across the stationary phase. Each substance in the mixture has their own inherent properties, which control attachment to the stationary phase at different locations (Figure 3.4). The location of this attachment is characteristic for the substance and serves as a beginning for the identification of the material.

Gas Chromatography

A gas chromatograph separates substances based on the chromatography principle described above. The stationary phase in this case is a liquid or solid that has been placed into a column packed with diatomaceous earth and the mobile phase is a gas. The unknown liquid or gas substance to be analyzed must be carried by the mobile gas and is deposited along the liquid or solid stationary column. This column separation causes the substances being analyzed to come out the other end at different rates. This is called elution rates. The amount of time the substance remains on the column is called retention time. Both the elution rate and the retention time are characteristic with each substance and can be used to identify the analyte. Elation and retention times are stored in a library database in a computer attached to the instrument. Comparison is made between the unknown material composition peaks to the database to establish the identity of the material.

Gas Chromatograph/Mass Spectrophotometer

This is known as the GC-MS. It works exactly like the above-described gas chromatograph but in addition has a mass spectrometer attached. The MS unit receives the substance as it exits the GC. It ionizes the substance and causes the substance to break down into smaller positively charged particles. Each substance breaks down in a characteristic fragmentation pattern because of its inherent properties. This pattern is used to identify the substance. Because of the complicated nature of this fragmentation pattern, this is done by computerization to find the proper identity within the 'computer library'.

ELECTROPHORESIS

Electrophoresis is a way of separating different molecules based on their charge. It usually uses a gel medium within a solvent and contains a negative charge on one side and a positive charge on the opposite side. The molecule needing separation is placed into a well in the gel near the negatively charged electrode. The current is applied and the particles with the negative charge migrate the quickest toward the positive charge and the positively charged particles remain closest to the negative electrode. After the migration is complete, the electricity is removed and the gel plate is developed by staining it with dyes or radioactive materials. Electrophoresis is the technique used to perform DNA typing. DNA typing is done on a specimen to determine individualizing characteristics, which are then entered into the FBI database (called CODIS).

AFIS

AFIS is the Automated Fingerprint Identification System.

The first year for the use of fingerprint identification was in 1902[3] and in 1924 the FBI fingerprint unit was established. The division of the FBI, which houses AFIS, contains over 80 million ten prints on file and receives over 7,000 new additions each day. If an agency submits prints to the system, a response to the prints is issued within 2 hours of receipt. This is a far cry of the initial methods of comparison prior to computerization where each ten card was compared by hand one to one via magnifying glass. AFIS works by reducing the image to a numerical pattern based on the ridge detail found in prints. In essence, AFIS is a huge computerized database of ridge details from fingerprints and catalogs these individualizing characteristics for comparison.

FIREARMS

Firearms are test fired into water tanks to retrieve bullets from suspect weapons and compare them to bullets retrieved from crime scenes. (Figure 3.5a & b) The lands and grooves engraved in bullets are characteristic to a specific weapon, much like fingerprints are characteristic of each person. The FBI also maintains a national database of bullet individualizing characteristics (called NIBIN).

Figure 3.5a Firearms testing water tank

Figure 3.5b Firearms testing water tank in use.

SUMMARY

This chapter discussed what evidence is, where and how it can be found, basic collection procedures, and how it is evaluated once it reaches the laboratory.

DISCUSSION TOPICS

Vocabulary

- cass characteristics
- individualizing characteristics
- biological evidence
- physical evidence
- chromatography
- gas chromatograph
- microscope
- electrophoresis
- GC-MS
- AFIS
- CODIS
- NIBIN
- control samples
- reference samples
- elimination samples

DISCUSSION QUESTIONS

1. List various pieces of evidence and characterize whether they are biologic or physical types.

2. Outline the major testing procedures discussed in the reading and the basis of how they work to produce test results.

3. Give examples of specimens that might be useful to examine with each of these testing procedures.

4. Define class and individualizing characteristics of evidence and describe three pieces of evidence with examples of individualizing and class of characteristics.

5. List the pertinent steps needed to properly label evidence.

ADDITIONAL READING

Without a trace. Advances in Detecting Trace Evidence
http://www.ncjrs.org/pdffiles1/jr000249b.pdf

Physical Evidence Bulletin
http://www.cci.ca.gov/Reference/peb/peb22.pdf

Forensics Tutorial: The Practical Applications of Light
http://www.mellesgriot.com/products/forensics/forensicstutorial.asp
This article reviews alternate light sources and has beautiful photo examples.

Pictures of the alternate light sources
http://www.mellesgriot.com/pdf/FRNSCBRO_PNLS.pdf

Crime Scene Investigation: A Reference for Law Enforcement Training
http://www.ncjrs.org/pdffiles1/nij/200160.pdf

Components of microscopes: light, polarizing, scanning electron microscopy (scanning em), transmission electron microscopy (transmission em)
http://homepages.gac.edu/cellab/chpts/chpt1/intro1.html

ENDNOTES

1. http://www.state.me.us/dps/msp/crimelab/evman.htm

2. http://www.cci.ca.gov/Reference/peb/peb22.pdf

3. http://www.fbi.gov/hq/cjisd/ident.pdf

Chapter 4

The Laboratory

OVERVIEW

This chapter covers crime laboratory jurisdictions, laboratory regulations, laboratory etiquette, laboratory capabilities and priority of testing.

CHAPTER OBJECTIVES

After studying this chapter, the student will be able to:
1. Understand the various laboratory jurisdictions and referral abilities.
2. Gain understanding of the various laboratory regulations and testing standards.
3. Become aware of proper laboratory etiquette.
4. Understand the various laboratory departments and their capabilities.
5. Understand the basis for prioritizing specimens.

HISTORICAL PERSPECTIVES

The American Society of Crime Laboratory Directors was established in 1976 to promote quality of practice in the forensic sciences and to provide training and direction to crime laboratories. The American Academy of Forensic Sciences also provides great support for research and sharing of ideas throughout the forensic disciplines. The FBI was formed in 1908 with the crime laboratory becoming an official component in 1932. (Figure 4.1) The FBI largely investigated bank crimes and fraud, but when the Mann Act of 1910 was passed, it became illegal to transport women across state lines for immoral purposes and crime investigation began to blossom. One of the first official cases of the laboratory was handwriting and typewriter analysis relating to a man who had been poisoned in a federal mental institution. The crime lab provided evidence that the note accompanying the poisoned candy had originated from the victim's sister's typewriter.

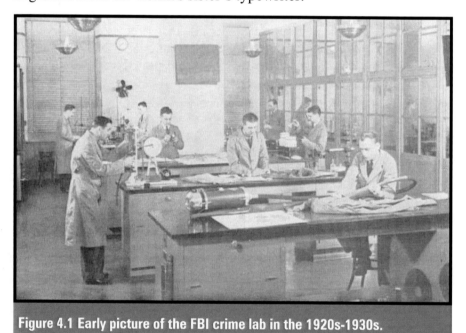

Figure 4.1 Early picture of the FBI crime lab in the 1920s-1930s.

REGULATION OF LABORATORIES

Quality Assurance Standards

Laboratories operate under the principle of providing quality results for accurate interpretation of scientific data. To ensure this, laboratories can be accredited by the American Society of Crime Laboratory Directors. (Accreditation is voluntary, not mandatory.) The accreditation process involves peer review of the policies, procedures, personnel qualifications and laboratory record keeping procedures by other crime laboratory directors to ensure that accurate results are reported. Quality assurance procedures take multiple forms within the laboratory to achieve this outcome. They include quality control, calibration and proficiency testing. These quality control procedures include running known controls (having a known range of values) with each batch of specimens. If the controls 'are in' (within the known set parameters for that test, usually a high and a low value) then the test results for the specimens (unknowns) are valid. If the controls do not work properly, there may be a problem with the instrument and it needs repair or the controls need to be updated. In addition, instruments are calibrated with known calibration materials provided by the instrument manufacturer. These calibration materials set the instrument's variables.

Other procedures are used to make sure one laboratory produces results comparable to another laboratory and are called proficiency standards. These require subscribing to testing services, which send various laboratory specimens as unknowns. The specimens are run on the instrument platform they were designed to test and the results are reported back to the testing center. All participating laboratory results are then 'passed' or 'failed' in their result. A failure in a result requires a corrective procedure and documentation of what the corrective action was. This is then filed and is usually reviewed by accreditation agencies.

If the frequency of failed results is too high, accreditation may be revoked or the laboratory may be put on probation until it again meets accreditation standards. This is why control procedures need to be monitored by the laboratory supervisors and repeated failures are reported to them. Test results cannot be reported unless they are valid. They are verified by control tests. The controls serve as day-to-day assurance that the laboratory is operating within compliance. Laboratories may take further action by implementing pooled patient specimens, which give them a tested known range. Another method that can be used is to submit a specimen from one laboratory to another is to compare results. These are inexpensive ways of testing and double-checking instrument values and procedures. Implementation of new testing procedure and instruments requires rigorous evaluation by the laboratory director prior to the patient test values being reported.

Standard Operating Procedures

To maintain rules of operation within the organization of the laboratory, the director institutes laboratory procedures (standard operating procedures). These procedures are in place to ensure laboratory safety, reproducibility of laboratory results, and are necessary for accreditation. Federal grants and other money may hinge on the laboratory's credibility and accreditation status. Therefore, it is important that the laboratory operate under the laboratory guidelines.

These procedures are based on tested scientific procedures from the literature or from the instrument manufacturer. Variance from a procedure may give misleading results. The results may be reported as 'normal' because of the deviation from a procedure but in actuality be abnormal if tested properly.

Some of the areas of the laboratory, for example the DNA portion, may be further regulated by other credentialing agencies. The DNA Identification Act of 1994 established the DNA Advisory Board that sets quality assurance standards for DNA profiling and entry into the FBI's CODIS system. These are included within the American Society of Crime Laboratory Directors, Laboratory Accreditation Board reviews.

CRIME LABORATORY JURISDICTIONS

There are over 400 crime laboratories in the United States operating at the city, county or state level. The only federal crime laboratory is the FBI. The FBI serves as a resource for the other laboratories to provide services that are unusual, require expertise not available at the state level or involve crimes crossing state lines and fall under the jurisdiction of the federal investigating agents. For many years, the local and state crime labs did not have capabilities to perform gunshot residue testing and it was referred commonly to the FBI for testing. Small jurisdictions may not have DNA testing capabilities and it is referred to the state crime laboratory for analysis.

LABORATORY ETIQUETTE

Laboratories operate under the safest principles possible to prevent health and safety hazards to its workers. They operate under the Occupational Safety & Health Administration (OSHA) guidelines for bloodborne pathogens. These are especially important because of the nearly constant exposure to biohazardous materials. Proper laboratory etiquette includes no eating, drinking or smoking within the laboratory area or where biohazardous materials are handled (crime scenes). This not only prevents contamination of the evidence but also prevents disease transmission to the laboratory personnel. To prevent contamination of the personnel's clothing, lab coats or personal protective equipment needs to be worn. Personal Protective Equipment (PPE) at a scene includes disposable paper coveralls, shoe covers, gloves, hair covers and masks. In the laboratory, this can be tailored to the degree of exposure to biohazardous materials and each area will have its own rules. In the laboratory, eyewear, gloves and lab coat are usually sufficient. Anytime blood can be aerosolized or spattered on someone, it is important to wear eyewear and masks. Lab coats are always a good idea to prevent 'taking work home with you' as contaminants on street clothing. Hepatitis B immunization is recommended to prevent acquiring Hepatitis B disease from exposure to contaminated secretions or body fluids. All secretions are treated as potentially infectious.

To prevent contamination of paperwork, the laboratory stations are usually divided into clean and dirty areas. The clean areas contain materials that can leave the laboratory without being disinfected. The dirty areas are those that have come into contact with biohazardous materials. The two should not cross, nor should dirty gloves touch clean paperwork that other personnel might touch without gloves and hence exposed to potential disease pathogens. Dirty areas need to be cleaned with disinfectant solutions between cases to prevent cross-contamination and deter bacterial growth in the laboratory.

All contaminated trash must be disposed of properly. Any biohazardous material must be disposed of in red biohazard bags. No food materials other than evidentiary disposal must be placed in these receptacles. They are also identified by the *biohazard symbol*. This trash must be disposed of through special companies dealing with this routinely and does not go to the landfill like ordinary trash.

Biohazard symbol

Proper hand washing techniques must also be adhered to. Prior to leaving any laboratory area, after removing gloves, it is important to wash hands with soap and water. At scenes, this is more difficult but can be accomplished with sanitizing solutions and washing hands as soon as conveniently possible. In all cases, it is advisable to adhere to good hand washing prior to eating outside the scene or laboratory.

CAPABILITIES OF A CRIME LABORATORY

The areas accredited by the ASCLD are controlled substances, toxicology, trace evidence, forensic biology/DNA, firearms/toolmarks, questioned documents and latent prints.[1]

Forensic Biology

The forensic biology portion of the laboratory deals with serology and DNA identification from a specimen. These portions utilize body fluids (blood, saliva, semen) to identify DNA, compare it to suspects or enter it into the FBI DNA database (CODIS) for potential identification. (Figure 4.2) Because of the huge demand for analysis, there are large backlogs of specimens waiting to be tested in many jurisdictions.

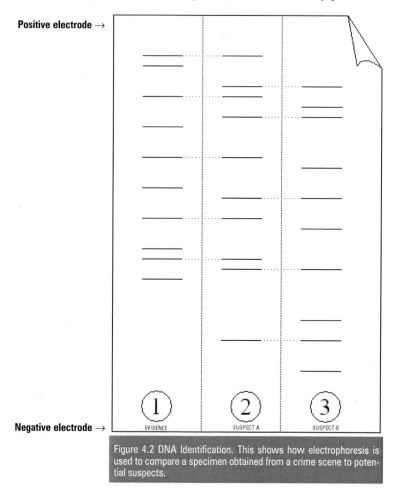

Positive electrode →

Negative electrode →

1 EVIDENCE   2 SUSPECT A   3 SUSPECT B

Figure 4.2 DNA Identification. This shows how electrophoresis is used to compare a specimen obtained from a crime scene to potential suspects.

The specimens are placed in the order noted above. The electric current is applied and the bands separate. Comparing the evidence channel banding pattern 1 with channels 2 & 3 shows a potential match to suspect A; and exclusion of suspect B.

Forensic Chemistry

This division deals with materials not analyzed in the other portions of the lab including hair classification and comparison, fiber analysis, glass, paint and accelerant evaluation. Another area within the chemistry division is controlled substances, which evaluates and analyzes potential drugs (heroine, cocaine, methamphetamine, prescription drugs etc) for identification but does not deal with toxicological analysis of biologic specimens.

Toxicology

This section evaluates biologic specimens (mainly blood and urine) for potential illicit drugs or alcohol in cases of driving under the influence. In some jurisdictions, drug analysis is performed for the medical examiner or coroner to determine the drug's role in the cause and manner of death. The instrumentation for the controlled substances and toxicology sections are usually very similar however, separate instruments are usually used because of the different concentrations and instrument parameters needed for each type of analysis.

Latent Prints

This division involves analysis of fingerprints. Most prints are not visible until some type of processing occurs. Fingerprint powder, lasers and superglue processing are among the most common. After retrieving the prints, they are identified by entry into the Automated Fingerprint Identification System (AFIS) which contains a known database of prints from previous arrests in the local, state and federal jurisdictions. (Figures 4.3a & 4.3b) This division also deals with comparison footwear and tire track impressions.

Figure 4.3a AFIS system and digital fingerprint analysis.

Figure 4.3b Latent print match using points of identification.

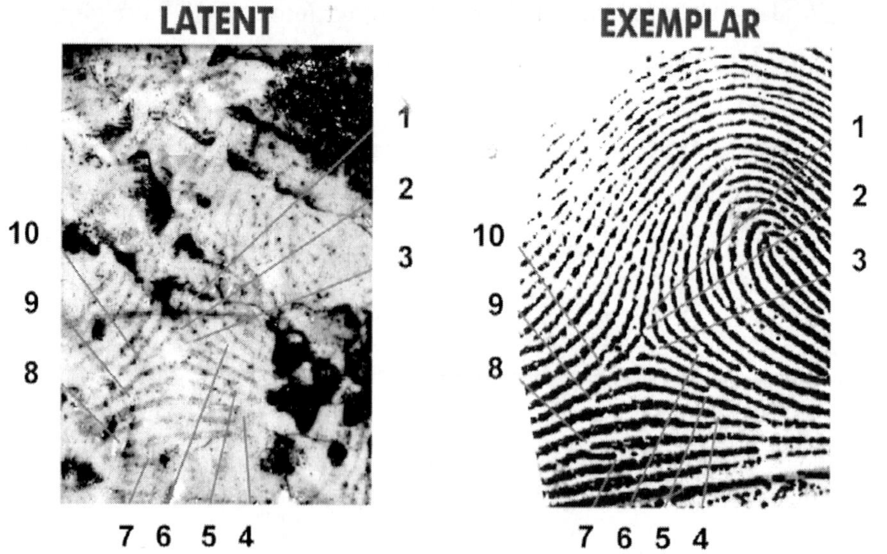

LATENT

EXEMPLAR

Firearms and Toolmarks

This section deals with firearms and weapons used to commit crimes. When a gun is fired, the weapon leaves characteristic marks on the bullet and bullet casing. A firearms examiner can associate weapons to bullets and casings by comparing them for a potential match under a comparison microscope. This data is also entered into the National Integrated Ballistic Identification Network (NIBIN), which can be used to facilitate the comparison of casings, projectiles and weapons and link them to different crime scenes across different law enforcement jurisdictions. Toolmarks are marks left by various objects and instruments on bodies or at crime scenes. The grooving by each tool can be individualized and compared to suspect weapons for identification.

Questioned Documents

This area involves handwriting analysis, evaluation of different documents and obliterated writing, paper and ink materials, comparison of typewritten material, counterfeit money analysis, restoration of damaged or altered documents.

Computer Forensics

This area deals with evaluation of computers and data within them, retrieval of erased data that may have been involved in criminal activity, pagers, cell phones and other electronic data devices.

Reconstruction

Some laboratories deal with reconstruction of a crime or motor vehicle accident. These professionals take data from multiple areas of the laboratory (blood type, DNA, blood spatter, bullet recovery, fingerprints, etc) and are able to hypothesize how a crime scene or motor vehicle accident may have occurred.

Photography

Photography has become an integral part of documentation of crime scenes. Traditionally, 35mm photography has been the standard or traditional type of imaging admitted as evidence in court. The advantages of digital photography are the ease of storage, reproducibility of images and the ability to determine the quality of an image at the time it was taken. The drawbacks to digital photography in the forensic world are the image resolution and questions about admissibility to court because of the ease digital photographs can be altered using software programs. Digital photographs are considered to meet the definition of evidence as electronic data materials but the rules for admissibility vary from state to state.

PRIORITIZING SPECIMENS

Specimen collection at a scene is a methodical search and retrieval procedure beginning with the evidence that may be destroyed by environmental conditions (heat, personnel, movement of victims, etc.) to evidence that is located on or under other evidence. The basic principle is to begin working from the outside edge of a scene and working inward, prioritizing specimens most in jeopardy. (Figure 4.4)

Some specimens will have more than one type of material on them that needs to be evaluated by the laboratory. Some of the evaluations are destructive to the specimen and it cannot be used for further analysis after that particular testing has been done. Other tests are not destructive to the specimen and further testing can be performed. Some specimen types are better suited for desired tests than others are. An example is fingerprinting evidence. Prints are very difficult to obtain from porous surfaces like bed sheets. Sheets are great specimens for obtaining DNA and trace evidence. Basically, each piece of evidence needs to be evaluated and triaged to the appropriate portion of the lab for the best return of evidence. The specimen is viewed from the most external portion to the internal portion, lifting the most external pieces of evidence first. An example is a baseball bat with blood spatter. Prints and DNA are both desired. Prints are most likely near the handle and can be viewed with alternate light sources for their location and retrieved in those areas. DNA and trace evidence can be harvested from the other areas. The use of luminol on the bat however, may preclude evaluation of prints or DNA as some of the compounds used can smear the prints or destroy the antigens used for DNA typing.

Figure 4.4 Prioritizing Evidence Collection at a Scene

- Conduct a careful and methodical evaluation considering all physical evidence possibilities (e.g., biological fluids, latent prints, trace evidence).
- Focus first on the easily accessible areas in open view and proceed to out-of-view locations.
- Select a systematic search pattern for evidence collection based on the size and location of the scene
- Select a progression of processing/collection methods so that initial techniques do not compromise subsequent processing/collections methods.
- Concentrate on the most transient evidence and work to the least transient forms of physical evidence.
- Move from least intrusive to most intrusive processing/collection methods.
- Continually assess environmental and other factors that may affect the evidence.
- Be aware of multiple scenes (e.g., victims, suspects, vehicles, locations).
- Recognize other methods that are available to locate, technically document and collect evidence (e.g., alternate light source, enhancement, blood pattern documentation, projectile trajectory analysis).

(Source: http://www.ncjrs.org/txtfiles1/nij/178280.txt)

SUMMARY

This chapter discussed the operation of a laboratory including laboratory protocols for testing, safety, quality assurance and accreditation. Major departments that compose a crime laboratory were also outlined.

DISCUSSION TOPICS

Vocabulary

- quality assurance
- controls in laboratory instrumentation
- PPE
- forensic biology
- ASCLD
- forensic chemistry
- serology
- AFIS
- NIBIN
- CODIS
- questioned documents
- firearms and toolmark division
- proficiency testing
- accreditation

DISCUSSION QUESTIONS

1. Outline the various divisions in the crime lab and their respective duties.
2. Discuss the process of procuring and prioritizing specimens at a scene.
3. List CODIS, AFIS, NIBIN, PPE, ASCLD and what each of them stands for.
4. List the types of quality assurance measures that are used to assure quality test results within a crime laboratory.
5. List the do's and don'ts covered in laboratory safety.

HISTORICAL PERSPECTIVES

Blood typing and its role in transfusion medicine was described in 1909 when Dr. Karl Landsteiner was trying to understand why some people survived after a blood transfusion and others died. He discovered the basis of the ABO typing system. It wasn't until 1940 that the Rh (Rhesus) system was also discovered by Dr. Landsteiner. He is attributed with contributing one of the most important breakthroughs in medicine and received a Nobel prize for these efforts.

For years, ABO, Rh, blood enzyme typing and secretor status were the basis of identifying blood characteristics and linking suspects to crime scenes. DNA typing was not introduced as a method of identification until 1985 when Dr. Alec Jeffries introduced the concept of 'genetic fingerprinting'.

CHARACTERISTICS OF BLOOD

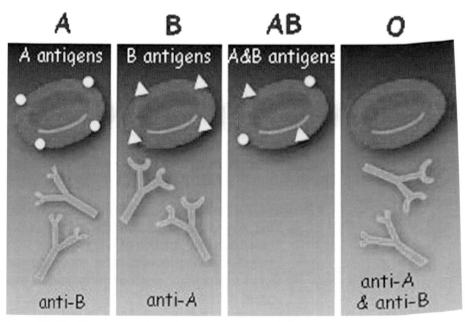

Image 5.1 Blood type as related to cell and plasma characteristics.

Blood is composed of cells and liquid in an approximate ratio of 40% cells to 60% liquid. The cells include red cells (RBC's), white cells (WBC's) and platelets. The white cells have subcategories: neutrophils, lymphocytes, monocytes, eosinophils and basophils. (Figure 5.1) All white cells have nuclei which characterize their appearance. Platelets and red cells do not have nuclei in their usual forms. Red cells appear as biconcave disks; platelets as small amorphous blobs.

The liquid is composed of a water-like substance called plasma. Plasma decreases the friction between the different cells and serves as a medium for the cells to circulate through the small channels of the body (capillaries). The plasma contains small amounts of minerals (sodium, potassium, chloride, calcium to name a few), hormones (thyroid hormone, adrenaline, estrogen, testosterone, etc.), antibodies and clotting factors. Normally as blood circulates, it is uncoagulated (not clotted). After an injury to a blood vessel, a series of reactions is initiated in the plasma, causing clotting factors to be released and adhesion of red cells and platelets to the injured site to prevent further bleeding. Externally, you may see this as a scab.

After blood is drawn from the body into a specimen tube, it naturally wants to clot much as if it were responding to an injured area of the body. In doing so, the cells (white, red and platelets) clump together. If the specimen is spun in a centrifuge, the cell portion separates from the liquid portion forming different layers. The liquid portion is then called serum, indicating that it arose from a previously clotted sample and has both the cells and clotting factors removed.

Some specimen tubes contain special chemicals called anti-coagulants (EDTA, heparin, sodium flouride) which prevent the initiation of the clotting cascade in the test tube. EDTA (ethylenediaminetetraacetic acid) prevents clotting by binding calcium ions in the blood which are needed for the clotting cascade mechanism. Heparin works by preventing protein conversion steps within the clotting sequence. Sodium fluoride inhibits certain enzymes in the blood and preserves it in a static state. Blood with these preservatives remains liquid and is called whole blood (containing all the components seen in circulating blood).

Some laboratory tests require whole blood and others require serum. This is because different testing methods used in the laboratory tests may be incompatible with the cells in whole blood so only the serum is used. On the other hand, some tests require the cell components and will utilize a whole blood specimen. Either way, it is not possible to convert a whole blood specimen in a tube to a serum specimen. The blood must be drawn from the patient properly and into the correct tube containing the corresponding preservative needed by the laboratory. Many times multiple tests can be performed on a single tube of blood. The laboratory should be consulted directly for the necessary volume of specimen needed to perform the combination of tests.

BLOOD CELLS

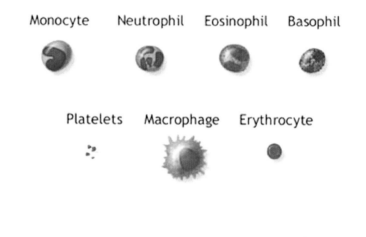

Image 5.2 Blood Cells

White Cells

Neutrophils

These cells function as the defense cells against bacteria. Some are always circulating in the blood and inactivating potential pathogens (disease carrying organisms) we may encounter in our daily lives. The neutrophils are formed from precursor cells (more primitive) in the bone marrow (center portion of bones like the femur or pelvis) of our body. These primitive cells are called 'stem cells' and are the precursors for all cells in our body.

Lymphocytes

These cells function as the defense cells against viruses. Like neutrophils, some are always circulating in the body to aid in our defense against the daily exposure to viruses in our environment. Their origin lies in the lymph nodes and an organ called the thymus. These cells are also important in the immunity of our bodies (self vs. non-self) and are important in the 'antigen-antibody response'. This means that the lymphocytes recognize foreign substances, by memory of previous exposure, and make antibodies against that substance. Antibodies are protein products made by the lymphocytes and circulate in the plasma with the purpose of attaching to a foreign protein and aiding in its destruction. Sometimes the antibody is helpful (for example, with strept throat, which is due to a bacterial infection) or can be detrimental (in heart transplants, the person's lymphocytes will see the proteins in the transplanted heart as foreign and try to destroy it).

Monocytes, Eosinophils and Basophils

Monocytes function in the cleanup of breakdown products from the neutrophils; eosinophils and basophils are involved in the allergic response to allergens (e.g., pollen).

Red Cells

Red cells contain the following materials which are important to our study of criminalistics:

Hemoglobin

This is a huge molecular protein capable of changing its properties so that it may carry oxygen from the lungs to the rest of the body or to carry carbon dioxide from the tissues to the lungs so that it may be discarded. This is a chemical type reaction and in some cases it goes awry. Other chemicals can bind to the oxygen site with greater affinity than oxygen and when it is time for it to be removed, it refuses and binds to the oxygen permanently. This renders that hemoglobin molecule inoperable of its function and eventually if enough of the cells are involved, the person will die. An example is carbon monoxide poisoning where the carbon monoxide molecule (inhaled in incomplete combustion such as house fires or car exhaust) binds to the hemoglobin molecule and replaces the oxygen. This binding by the carbon monoxide molecule creates a loss of oxygen to the body tissues.

Carbon monoxide binding to hemoglobin is a very firm type but can be reversed if the hemoglobin is exposed to high pressure oxygen concentrations. This can be achieved by the use of a hyperbaric chamber and is the treatment for carbon monoxide victims who are found alive. Cyanide inhalation (as in the gas chamber or from house fires) also affects the oxygen carrying capacity of blood. Its alteration is a permanent one and cannot be reversed like carbon monoxide inhalation can. Hemoglobin in its oxygenated state is responsible for the red appearance of blood. The protein units comprising hemoglobin are situated around a central atom of iron.

Surface Antigens on the Red Cell

These antigen sites are what determine our blood type. Antigens are small sequences of protein that are attached to the cell membrane (composed of protein + lipids {fats}). The antigen proteins have a particular unique sequence which is where the different blood types, i.e. A, B, O, and AB are characterized. With Rh factor, an additional protein is also present. If one is Rh+ (Rh positive) this surface protein is present; if one is Rh- (Rh negative) this protein is absent.

CONCEPT OF ANTIGENS AND ANTIBODIES

The concept of antigens and antibodies is important in the study of blood and is a principle utilized extensively in the laboratory. It began as a study of the response of the human body to 'foreign' material, meaning that the substance is not something seen or known by the body prior to it being introduced into it. The body has an innate sense of knowing what products or cells are made by it (HLA antigens) and senses these markers present on the surface of all cells. As a protective mechanism, our body developed a defense system against foreign materials, i.e. the production of antibodies. Antibodies are proteins made by the lymphocytes and are specific for each foreign substance. They circulate in the plasma in small numbers and if exposed to a foreign substance for a second time, the body gears up the production of antibodies against that particular substance in an effort to contain and destroy it before it does damage. Antibodies form against bacteria, proteins (allergens, transplants), viruses etc.

Many years ago, the laboratory recognized the value of this reaction. A protein can be tested for by reacting with a manmade antibody and the new compound detected by a laboratory instrument. A totally negative result (i.e., no protein of the type being tested) can be detected by the absence of binding between the antigen (protein) and the antibody. Because the reaction is occurring on a small molecular level, the manmade antibody is usually attached to a marker of some sort. This can be a marker that changes color when the antibody attaches or a change in the amount or type of a radioactive substance. The amount of color change is then measured and a quantifying value is attached to the reaction. Some reactions can be qualitative, i.e. not given a specific value, only a positive or negative one, and these are useful screening tests.

BLOOD TYPING

Blood typing is characterized by two parameters: the antigen on the red cell surface and circulating antibodies in the plasma. (Figure 5.2) These circulating antibodies are protective mechanisms to prevent infusion of foreign red cells into the body and act to destroy red cells of other blood types.

Type A

Type A blood is defined as red cells containing the 'A' antigen (protein) on its' red cell surface. The plasma contains anti-B (antibody against B antigen on red cell surfaces).

Type B

Type B blood is defined as red cells containing the 'B' antigen on the red cell surface. The plasma contains anti-A (antibody against A antigen on red cell surfaces).

Type O

Type O blood is defined as cells containing neither the 'A' nor the 'B' antigen on the person's red cells. It contains both anti-A and anti-B (antibodies to both A and B antigens on red cell surfaces) in the plasma. In transfusion medicine, usually the red cells are given; transfusions do not include the plasma. Because the Type O cells contain neither of the antigens, these persons are considered "universal donors" as their red cells will not react against either Type A or Type B persons circulating antibodies. Type O is the most common. (Figure 5.1)

Figure 5.1 Blood Type Chart
Type O = Universal donor: The absence of red cell antigens allows type O negative to be given to all blood types. Type AB = Universal recipient: The presence of both A&B red cell antigens allow Type AB to receive any blood type in a transfusion.

If your blood type is...	You can receive....			
AB+	any blood type			
AB-	O-	A-	B-	AB-
A+	O-	O+	A-	A+
A-	O-	A-		
B+	O-	O+	B-	B+
B-	O-	B-		
O+	O-	O+		
O-	O-			

©2004 The American Red Cross. Reprinted with permission.

Type AB

Type AB blood is defined as red cells containing both 'A' and 'B' antigens on their surface. Because it has both antigens on the cells, it cannot have antibodies in the serum or the red cells would be destroyed. So the anti-A and anti-B antibodies are absent in type AB plasma. These people are considered "universal recipients" because they can accept cells with the 'A' or 'B' antigen on the surface as they do not have circulating antibodies to either type. This blood type is the least common. (Figure 5.2)

Figure 5.2 Blood Typing in the Laboratory	
Out of every 100 people in the United States...	
38 have O positive blood	7 have O negative blood
34 have A positive blood	6 have A negative blood
9 have B positive blood	2 have B negative blood
3 have AB positive blood	1 has AB negative

©2004 The American Red Cross. Reprinted with permission.

Blood Typing Procedures

Procedures used by the laboratory to determine a specimen's blood type utilize the principles of antigen-antibody testing. Artificial antibodies are made in animals or by laboratory methods thru recombinant DNA procedures. These antibodies are produced for each of the antigens involved in testing (anti-A, anti-B, anti-Rh). The antibodies are proteins immersed in a saline solution. Anti-A, anti-B and anti-Rh are mixed on separate slides with the unknown blood type and observed for binding which is visualized as clumping of the red cells. Clumping is considered a positive result; no clumping is a negative result. If someone is Type A and mixed with anti-A and anti-B sera, you would expect clumping of the A sera and none with the B. Similarly, Type B when mixed with the sera would result in clumping with the B sera and no clumping with the A. Type O would show no clumping with either anti-A or anti-B and Type AB would show clumping with both. The clumping occurs at the individual cell level with binding of the antibodies between multiple red cells. After enough red cells are bound, the clumping can be visualized with the naked eye and a microscope is not needed.

HEREDITY

Each individual has 46 chromosomes plus an X and another X or Y (the latter are the sex chromosomes, XX=female; XY=male) the full complement of chromosomes is found in all cells with nuclei except for the eggs and sperm cells. Half of a person's heredity comes from their mother (23 chromosomes + X) and half from their father (23 chromosomes + X or Y). The mother always supplies one of her 2 X chromosomes to the offspring and the father can supply either an X or a Y. Hence, the father determines the gender of the child. The chromosomes make up our individual DNA (deoxyribonucleic acid) makeup. DNA is stored in the nucleus of cells and code for all the proteins that make up the cells and their products. To get the DNA message to the factories (ribosomes) in the cytoplasm, the cell uses a messenger called RNA (ribonucleic acid) to serve as a copy of the nuclear DNA and carries it to the cytoplasm.

The cytoplasm contains a number of organelles, including one called mitochondria, which is known as the power plant of the cells. Each mitochondria stores another copy of the DNA called mitochondrial

DNA (mDNA). This copy of a person's DNA is unique in that it only contains a copy of the maternal DNA, is in a ring form rather than the crossed and paired form visualized in nuclear DNA. This is important when we discuss DNA technology as it is sometimes necessary to perform mitochondrial DNA testing which would only reflect the maternal source.

Chromosomes are composed of DNA which is a double helical structure (basically a spiral staircase) composed of sequences of proteins and sugars. Groups of DNA are called genes and these groups comprise enough protein and sugar base pairs to create individual protein products, like hair color, eye color etc.

Since we carry two copies of each chromosome (one from the mother, one from the father), there is a chance of blending the expressed trait or one trait to express dominance over the other. This is gene specific and varies according to the trait that is being discussed. An example of how this works is below:

A mother has brown eyes and a father has blue eyes. Blue eyes are recessive, brown eyes are dominant. The mother had a father with blue eyes and a mother with brown eyes so she is BrBl (a gene from each); the father carries both blue traits: Bl, Bl (both his parents had blue eyes). The offspring of the BrBl mother and the Bl, Bl father are half brown eyed (Br,Bl) and half blue eyed (Bl,Bl) children. If the mother had had a mother with Brown eyes and both dominant traits were present (Br,Br) then her offspring with the blue eyed (Bl,Bl) father would all have brown eyes (Br,Bl).This is the concept of Mendelian genetics where one trait is said to be dominant and expressed over another (called recessive).

Blood typing is also characterized by Mendelian genetics. Two genes, one inherited from your mother and one from your father, characterize your blood type. The A and B genes are both dominant, O genes are recessive. Type A blood is characterized genetically by AA or AO depending on the parents of the offspring; Type B is BB or BO; Type O by definition must be OO; Type AB is just that, one gene from each parent, AB. (Figure 5.3)

Figure 5.3 Blood Type Inheritances

Parents' Blood Types	Children's Possible Blood Types			
AB + AB	AB	A	B	
AB + A	AB	A	B	
AB + B	AB	A	B	
AB + 0		A	B	
A + A		A		0
A + B	AB	A	B	0
B + B			B	0
0 + A		A		0
0 + B			B	0
0 + 0				0

©2004 The American Red Cross. Reprinted with permission.

Secretor Status

About 80 to 85% of the population secrete their blood type in body secretions such as saliva, sweat and semen and are known commonly as secretors. Prior to DNA testing, linking a person to a crime scene was done by ABO typing, typing blood for certain enzymes and testing their secretor status. DNA has made this type of testing obsolete but this previous methodology is the basis for current post-conviction testing by DNA. Some prisoners claim they were convicted unjustly based on the traditional typing. Motions for retesting of evidence based on the new DNA technology has allowed some of the previously convicted to go free. The technology also has proven that many more had a positive match of their DNA with the scene evidence. Supported convictions don't seem to get as much press. Blood is not considered a piece of evidence that can be positively linked to an individual, even with DNA. Its admissibility is based on population statistics and the likelihood that the blood evidence is linked to a particular subject rather than it being positively linked to someone. This is in contrast to linking evidence such as a bullet to a particular gun.

COLLECTING BLOOD AT A SCENE

When confronted with the possibility of blood at a scene, the question, "Is it blood?" will need to be addressed first. If it is blood, "Is it human or non-human blood?" After a specimen is found to be blood,

blood typing is done for screening. Then if necessary, DNA is performed but at greater cost and time.

Is It Blood?

Blood at a scene may be obvious or cleaned up and not obvious. All animals contain the basic structure of hemoglobin within their red cells. Hemoglobin has natural peroxide like activity. Reagent impregnated sticks (called Hemastix®) are commercially available and take advantage of this activity. Compounds such as guaiac, are used as the reagent and when they come in contact with hemoglobin a visible color change occurs, usually from tan to blue or green. The color change signifies the presence of blood but does not differentiate the species of origin, i.e. animal from human. (Image 5.3)

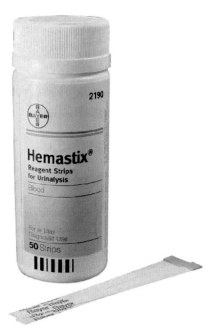

Image 5.3 Hemastix®. These sticks are useful to detect the presence of blood and are positive for blood when the color changes from yellow to green. Permission by Lynn Peavey Co. & Bayer Corp.

Another test in use is the Kastle-Meyer Test. This utilizes phenolphthalein which reacts with the peroxidase in hemoglobin in the presence of hydrogen peroxide to create a pink color. It is sensitive to the presence of blood but shows false positives with potatoes and horseradish.[1]

Is it Human or Non-Human?

To answer this question the lab uses an antibody-antigen reaction. Human blood is injected in small quantities into rabbits. The rabbits create antibodies to the human blood because they see it as foreign (anti-human Ab). These antibodies are harvested and used to react with an unknown blood stain. The reaction of the two creates a cloudy band either at the interface of the two in a liquid form or over the surface of a gel. In the latter, the anti-human antibody is placed in one well and the unknown blood in an adjacent one. Natural diffusion will cause them to move toward one another and form a band if human blood is present. If non-human blood is present, no precipitation line will form. The same principles can be used to create and test for the origin of any species by using created antibodies to a particular animal.

Enhancement of Blood Stains

There are methods available to make blood stains more apparent than the naked eye can see. One way is through the use of alternate light sources. These instruments utilize wave lengths outside the usual household spectra to visualize evidence. Alternate light sources with variable wave lengths are available in addition to laser light sources which are focused monochromatic beam of light. Ultraviolet (UV) light is useful to identify semen stains and this will be talked about in a later chapter. Other wave lengths are useful to visualize fingerprints and trace evidence such as fibers.

Luminol

Another method is to use special chemicals to enhance the visibility of faint or previously existing blood. Luminol is a chemiluminescent compound that emits light as it changes from one chemical form to another. This transformation is aided by compounds called catalysts (a metal or enzyme which make a reaction occur more quickly because of its presence). Of the known catalysts for luminol, one is iron found in hemoglobin. The reaction is very sensitive and requires very little hemoglobin for the luminol to glow. Luminol is mixed and sprayed as an aerosol over a surface. An area where blood has been cleaned and diluted can still be identified even years after the incident. With special camera settings, the chemiluminescent glow and pattern can be photographed.

Luminol use does have some drawbacks. Luminol has been found to interfere with subsequent DNA testing. There are false positives that react with luminol such as bleach, dyes, some vegetation or other items that contain the metal catalysts iron, cobalt or copper. Its water base can cause smearing of fingerprints or shoe imprints. Because of these issues, it is advised that luminol not be the first resource used to detect blood. (http://www.crime-scene-investigator.net/blood.html). It is better to first use alternate light sources to locate the stains and collect them.

COLLECTION OF BLOOD STAINS

The collection of the stain depends on the surface it is on and the condition of the specimen. Collection also includes proper labeling of the specimen and chain of custody.

Labeling and Chain of Custody

All evidence needs to be placed in a suitable container and labeled with the location of its retrieval, case number, address, date, time and who collected it. It is usually given a letter or number as an identifier to locate it within the scene, then logged onto a list with a brief description. The list is then signed and submitted to the lab as evidence where it is signed for by laboratory personnel. The process of signing evidence from one person to another is called chain of custody. This documentation is critical for the accountability of the evidence and forms the basis of its admissibility in court. Nothing should go from point A to point B without a signature to ensure the integrity of the evidence.

Hard Surfaces

A hard surface such as concrete, countertop or walls does not lend itself to excising a portion and submitting it to the lab. On the other hand, a motor vehicle with blood on the outside may be impounded and evidence retrieved within a closed environment. Collection of evidence in the latter scenario is limited to those areas that might be lost during transport. Other specimens such as doors might be better suited to submission in its entirety as it may contain other evidence (fingerprints, gunshot holes, hair) that need to be evaluated in addition to the blood evidence.

In general, a dried specimen on a surface can be collected two ways. It can be scraped off, using a scalpel, onto a clean filter paper or lab tissue and then placed in an envelope. If it is on a slightly rough surface like concrete, scraping may not work and a moistened swab rubbed over the stain will retrieve it. Sterile saline poured into a small disposable cup works well; the swabs are rolled over the upper edge of the cup to extrude the majority of water. Rolling the dampened swab over the dried spot in question preserves the evidence in a fashion suitable for DNA testing. Because it is moist, the swab will need to dry or be placed in a breathable paper envelope to prevent bacterial overgrowth. To prevent bleeding through, a small square of wax paper over the tip may be considered. The biggest offenders of DNA specimens are moisture, bacteria, mold and cross- contamination. Therefore, the damp swab might be easier to collect but has a higher degree of risk for preservation of the evidence.

Sterile saline or distilled water is used over tap water because it is not contaminated by bacteria (like tap water) and sterile saline resembles the physiologic properties blood has in the body (unlike distilled water). Distilled water will work if the integrity of the red cells is not needed (as in DNA testing). Because saline/distilled water is usually supplied in quarts or gallons, it is necessary to pour some out into a small sterile container. This prevents contamination of the main supply and carryover to the next scene or even from one area of the current scene to another. If you contaminate the small container, you have more to turn to. It is always a good practice to pour from your storage container into a smaller one, no matter what the chemical is, as it prevents contamination of your source. Be sure to wipe the scalpel clean between collection areas to prevent carry-over.

Porous Surface

Porous surfaces such as clothing, fabric from furniture or carpeting is better collected by cutting out sections and submitting them with the blood still in the surface. This allows the lab to have abundance of material to work with and prevents any mishandling of the specimen. If that is not feasible, the dampened swab can be done.

Easily removable objects like sheets, pillows or clothing are better suited to submission in their entirety. These are gently folded and placed into brown paper bags and taped closed with evidence tape. The bag is appropriately labeled.

Wet specimens can be collected either with a dry swab or absorbed onto a clean dry square of cloth or filter paper.

The method used in how to submit the specimen will be determined by the laboratory operating procedure, the officer in charge at the scene, the kind of case it is and the collaboration between the officer and the crime scene unit. When in doubt collect it. You only get one chance to collect material and after that, it is changed forever or is uncollectible. If you see something that was missed as possible evidence, discuss it with the officer in charge. Think on your feet, speak to the lab and get feedback as to the best way to collect something if it is difficult or unusual in some way.

Controls

The laboratory works on the principle of controls. These specimens are considered baseline and an unknown is compared to baseline to see if it is different in some way. Many times the difference between the known and unknown is what makes a test read as positive or negative. The importance of this concept is each laboratory test has an inherent false-positive rate, meaning it will read positive when it is actually negative. By using a control, it minimizes this false reading.

Collection of controls is important. They need to be collected in proximity to the desired specimen but far enough removed so that it does not contain the specimen. It also is collected in the same fashion as the unknown specimen. If a wet swab is used, then a wet swab is used in an area adjacent to, but not involving the specimen (i.e., a wet blood spot on a linoleum floor is collected with a swab; an adjacent area of the linoleum without blood should be swabbed as a control for the floor).

COLLECTION OF BLOOD FROM DECEDENTS

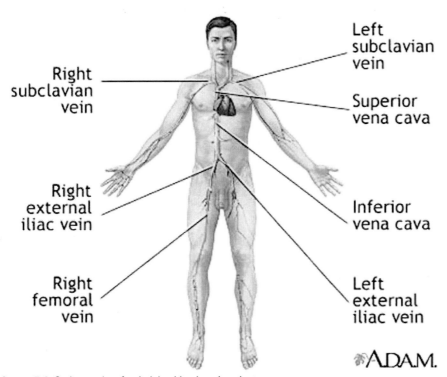

Image 5.4 Optimum sites for draining blood on decedents.

Generally this takes on two forms, hospital specimens and blood from decedents at the time of autopsy. Hospital specimens are ones drawn by medical care personnel during the attempts to save the person's life. These specimens are key evidence items as they most closely reflect the condition of the person at the time an injury or illness occurred. The most critical ones are the first specimens prior to any transfusions, intravenous fluids or drug administration. Any of these factors mask the quantitative and sometimes qualitative analysis. Intravenous fluids dilute the blood volume. Drugs administered by medical personnel can mask the issue of whether the drug was taken before or during the resuscitation, especially if they are narcotics. Blood transfusions not only dilute the specimen, but also change the DNA makeup of the decedent's blood. They no longer show a single DNA pattern but a mixture depending on how many different donor blood units were used. The life of a red cell is 120 days and it can take up to that long to return to the native DNA pattern.

Hospitals are accustomed to releasing specimens to law enforcement and medical examiner personnel. Many times, it requires a subpoena or standard release on letterhead from the agency requesting them. The most important aspect is to make an inventory of the specimens, including the number and type of tubes (usually descriptive is sufficient, i.e. purple top, red top, etc.), verify the name on the tube and that it belongs to the person you are seeking, the date and the time of collection. A chain of custody is imperative from the hospital, to the investigator, to the lab. It is usually best not to freeze blood specimens as the cells will rupture. Serum and urine can be frozen. Transport should occur in a cooler with cooler blocks, but do not freeze or leave them in a vehicle for a period of time or they will decompose. They should be transported from the hospital to the laboratory immediately to prevent deterioration of the specimens or questions regarding the integrity of the chain of custody. Policies vary from one hospital laboratory to another but most of them retain blood specimens for 3 to 7 days after they are drawn. The blood bank portion of the laboratory many times has the only specimen tube (purple top) that is suitable for DNA use. Urine is usually not retained more than 24 hours.

Specimens from decedents who are autopsied usually have blood drawn by the medical examiner. Typical sites of retrieval of blood from decedents include the femoral vein, iliac vein, inferior vena cava, subclavian vein or heart (cardiac). (Figure 5.4) The last site, cardiac blood is the least desirable as it is thought not to represent the best drug values and can be altered postmortem by the breakdown of cells.

It is standard operating procedure to draw any needed specimens for law enforcement upon their request. Many times, it is drawn by the medical examiner with the expectation that law enforcement will request it. Homicides and traffic accident victims usually have a purple top (whole blood specimen; purple tops contain EDTA anticoagulants) tube drawn and signed over to the investigating officer at the completion of the autopsy along with any other evidence. A purple top is also standard submission with a sexual assault kit and in both instances is used to obtain the blood or DNA type of the specimen. Because of the importance of DNA typing, most medical examiners' offices draw and hold a DNA specimen in the form of blood droplets dried on a filter paper, stored in envelopes and frozen. This form of blood preservation is thought to be good for at least 20 years. Liquid blood in specimen tubes has an expiration date and depends partially on the degree of bacterial contamination at the time the specimen is obtained. Whenever possible, the dried specimen should be obtained to use as a backup in case something happens to the liquid tube (some of these glass tubes do get dropped, broken or the top pops off). Gray top tubes contain sodium fluoride as a preservative and are typically used for toxicology testing. Red top tubes contain no preservatives or anticoagulants (so the blood clots, then is spun to retrieve the serum layer) and are used for tests such as HIV or hepatitis. (Images 5.5, 5.6 & 5.7. Red top tubes not shown.).

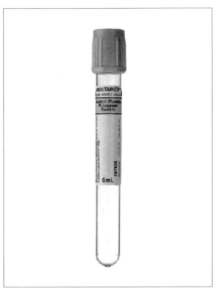

Image 5.5 Vacutainer® Purple Top tubes contains EDTA preservative and is useful for DNA testing. Photo permission: Becton Dickinson & Co.

Image 5.6 Vacutainer® Gray Top tubes contain sodium fluoride and are useful for toxicology testing. Photo permission: Becton Dickinson & Co.

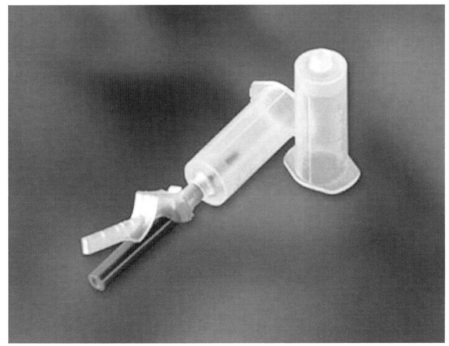

Image 5.7 Needle sleeve. Photo permission: Becton Dickinson & Co.

COLLECTION OF BLOOD FROM LIVING SUBJECTS

Before drawing a specimen on a live subject, it is necessary to get their written consent or obtain a court order to do so. The specimens are usually drawn by authorized phlebotomists, technicians who are trained to draw blood from patients. Most police departments also have phlebotomists on call to be utilized in obtaining specimens from subjects. Whenever drawing toxicology specimens that might include alcohol levels, the skin should never be cleansed with alcohol or alcohol wipes as it might contaminate the specimen causing elevated readings. Betadine swabs are the cleanser of choice. After the desired specimens are obtained, it is important that they are labeled properly by the person collecting them including the name of the subject, date and time of the specimen. A chain of custody is initiated and utilized from the phlebotomist to the investigator transporting the specimen and by the lab personnel who accept the specimen into the laboratory. It is important that whole blood specimens are transported cool but not frozen.

WHAT IS AN ADEQUATE SPECIMEN?

An adequate specimen is dictated by the laboratory and what testing is being requested. Depending on how many tests are being requested, mandates how many tubes and what kind of tubes will be needed. This is somewhat laboratory dependent. However, generalizations include: 1 purple top for DNA; at least 2, and preferably 3 grey tubes if the laboratory does whole blood testing for toxicology and urine, if available.

The specimen tubes in widest use are ones which contain an internal vacuum. These work in conjunction with a needle attached to a plastic holder. The specimen tube is inserted into the holder and pushed over the needle. The internal vacuum contains a lower pressure than the vein allowing the blood to pour into the tube. When the vacuum is relieved, the tube will stop filling and can be replaced with another tube without having to repuncture the vein. Red top or serum tubes do not contain preservatives or anticoagulants. Many contain a plastic plug in the center called a serum separator tube. This device functions as a barrier between the clotted cells and the serum after centrifugation to prevent leakage of the cell contents into the serum. This works on many hospital tests, but it is not the most desirable serum specimen for forensic toxicology. The separator tube has been known to absorb some drugs and prevent proper quantification and identification. It is best to have serum specimens drawn in a plain red top. This is not to say that if there is the only specimen available from a specific date and time, that it should be discarded. It still should be seized, but know that when given a choice, a better specimen type exists.

Those tubes with anticoagulant, such as EDTA or heparin, have different problems. The amount of preservative is based on the tube being full, usually a volume of 7cc. of blood. Lower volumes of blood can create problems in the specimen when it is being analyzed in the laboratory. It is best to allow each tube to fully fill prior to removing it from the needle. It is then gently inverted 4 or 5 times to allow mixture of the anticoagulant with the blood and prevent clots from forming (do not shake as it lyses or ruptures the cells).

SUMMARY

In this chapter, the following topics have been discussed: components of blood, blood typing, heredity factors, collection of blood specimens both from the live and dead subjects and the proper handling of blood specimens to maintain their integrity for laboratory testing and admissibility to court.

DISCUSSION TOPICS

Vocabulary

- plasma
- serum
- anti-coagulant
- chromosome
- gene
- antigen
- antibody
- DNA
- cell membrane
- mitochondria
- universal donor
- universal recipient
- gray top specimen tube
- purple top specimen tube
- red top specimen tube
- chain of custody
- control specimen
- hemoglobin
- lysis

DISCUSSION QUESTIONS

1. Identify the different components of blood and their functions.
2. Discuss the antigen-antibody reaction and its importance in laboratory testing.
3. Discuss blood typing and how the different blood types are arrived at in the laboratory.
4. Discuss proper collection techniques in the live subject.
5. Discuss proper collection techniques of the dried specimen at a scene.
6. Discuss proper collection techniques of the wet specimen at a scene.
7. Discuss proper collection techniques in the dead subject.
8. Discuss proper transport and handling of blood and biological specimens to the laboratory.
9. Discuss enhancement techniques for identifying blood at a scene.
10. Discuss dried blood specimens and the advantages for possible DNA use.

ADDITIONAL READING

Blood types
    http://en.wikipedia.org/wiki/Blood_type
Red blood cells
    http://en.wikipedia.org/wiki/Red_blood_cells
White blood cells
    http://en.wikipedia.org/wiki/White_blood_cells
Mendelian genetics
    http://en.wikipedia.org/wiki/Mendelian_genetics
Antigen
    http://en.wikipedia.org/wiki/Antigen
Antibody
    http://en.wikipedia.org/wiki/Antibody
Histocompatibility (idea of sameness in our bodies)
    http://en.wikipedia.org/wiki/Histocompatibility
Human leukocyte antigen (idea of sameness in our bodies)
    http://en.wikipedia.org/wiki/Human_leukocyte_antigen
Vacuum assisted blood tubes
    http://en.wikipedia.org/wiki/Vacutainer
Collection techniques utilized at the Louisiana State Crime Laboratory
    http://www.crime-scene-investigator.net/blood.html

ENDNOTES

1. *A Study of the Sensitivity and Specificity of Four Presumptive Tests for Blood*; M. Cox, Journal of Forensic Sciences, Vol. 36, No. 5, Sept. 1991, pp. 1503-1511.)

Chapter 6

Semen

OVERVIEW

In this chapter the components of semen, collection of specimens and specimen handling will be covered.

CHAPTER OBJECTIVES

After studying this chapter, the student will be able to:
1. Understand the components of semen.
2. Understand the procedure of collecting a sexual assault kit.
3. Understand the different procedures used to collect semen stains at a scene.
4. Understand the anatomy of spermatozoa and the location of DNA material.

HISTORICAL PERSPECTIVES

Semen became a forensic evidence tool after the discovery that 60% of men secrete their blood type in semen and other body secretions. These people are called 'secretors' and were able to be linked or vindicated as suspects based on the blood type and other enzymes found on the sperm cells. This technology would narrow a group of suspects by blood type, followed by other evidence (i.e., hairs or shoe imprints) to further delineate the suspect. The data obtained could narrow the suspect pool to hundreds. In 1985, DNA technology was discovered and provided a reasonable means of testing. DNA has the ability of testing very small sample sizes and is more specific than ABO or enzyme typing. It characterizes a semen stain to a population size of 1: billion when multiple markers are used.

CHARACTERISTICS OF SEMEN

Components of Semen

Semen is composed of sperm (5%) and secretions supplied by the seminal vesicles (60%) and prostate gland (20%). (Image 6.1)

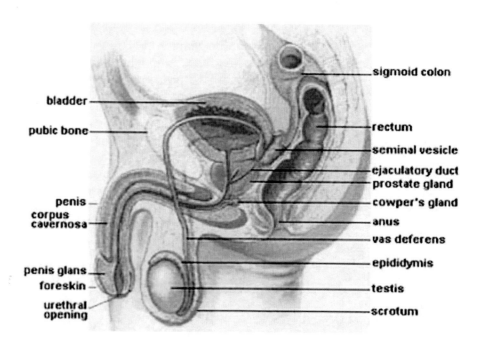

Image 6.1 Anatomy of the male genital tract.

Sperm are formed in the testes and stored in the epididymus. A vasectomy or sterilization procedure removes a portion of the vas deferens and interrupts the migration of the sperm from the epididymus to the ejaculate. In these men, the ejaculate no longer contains sperm but still contains the secretions from the prostate and seminal vesicles which form the majority of the ejaculate. The seminal vesicles secrete fructose, the sugar necessary for the ejaculate, and the pigments responsible for the fluorescence of semen under ultraviolet light (also called a Wood's lamp). The prostate secretions are responsible for the addition of acid phosphatase which is a useful indicator for the presence of semen and can be tested for in the laboratory.

The morphology of sperm includes a head and a tail. The tail is responsible for the sperm's motility in its efforts to fertilize the female egg. As sperm deteriorates, the head and tail may become separated. Sperm may remain motile up to 24 hours after ejaculation. However, the environment of the female cervix is conducive for them to be motile only a very short time (3 to 4 hours). (Image 6.2)

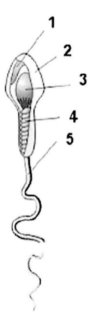

Image 6.2 Schematic diagram of a sperm cell, showing the (1) acrosome, (2) cell membrane, (3) nucleus, (4) mitochondria and (5) flagellum (tail)

The sperm head contains the nucleus with half the man's DNA content, 23 chromosomes and an X or Y chromosome. This portion can be used to identify the source of semen in a sexual assault case.

COLLECTING SEMEN AT A SCENE

The pigments present in semen have the ability to fluoresce under ultraviolet light. This principle is utilized at a scene to locate possible stains for collection. This is a useful tool, however, it is not infallible. If a stain looks suspicious for dried semen but doesn't fluoresce, collect it anyway.

Semen on Porous Surfaces

Semen may be located on clothing, bed sheets or other porous surfaces. These specimens are best collected whole (i.e., bed sheets) or portions cut out for submission and evaluation by the laboratory (e.g., carpet). It is important that these materials be placed in breathable containers to preserve the specimen for possible DNA and prevent mold or mildew on damp items. Sheets can be carefully folded inward to preserve the stain and any other adherent trace evidence such as hairs. Brown paper bags work best to transport them from the scene to the laboratory. It is important to close the bags with evidence tape and appropriately label each item with the location the item was recovered, the case number, date, time and who collected it. If the item is wet or damp, it may be necessary to place the items in evidence drier to prevent deterioration. These driers blow cool air across the materials and appear much like small closets or lockers to prevent cross contamination.

Semen on Non-collectible Surfaces

Sometimes a potential stain is located on a surface that cannot be removed to the laboratory. These stains can be collected much like blood stains by using a sterile swab dampened with saline and rolled gently over the stain. A second dry swab can be rolled over the same area and placed in a sterile envelope.

If the stain is thick enough, it may be possible to scrape it up with a sterile scalpel, placed onto a filter paper, then into an envelope.

Control Specimens

As in all laboratory specimen collections, a control swab or fabric needs to be obtained adjacent to the visibly stained area. This allows any background interference to be taken into consideration when interpreting the specimen results.

COLLECTING SEMEN FROM A LIVING OR DEAD SUBJECT

Sexual assault examinations are performed by a physician or a trained licensed practitioner. A standard sexual assault kit is collected and the investigator receives information from the care provider and the victim. It is important that the specimens be dried prior to placing them into the kit and that the kit contain known specimens from the victim. These known samples include head hair, pubic hair and a purple top for typing (both ABO and DNA) of the victim. The kit contains the following components:

- Brown bag for underwear
- Brown bag for clothing
- Pubic hair combings
- Known head hair pulls (50 hairs needed)
- Known pubic hair pulls (50 hairs needed)
- Oral swabs (2) and a microscopic slide for an oral swab smeared over the slide
- Vaginal swabs (2) plus the microscopic slide smear
- Anal swabs (2) plus the microscopic slide smear
- Purple top for blood (do not freeze as it will rupture)

This kit is adequate but gives very little room for dilute or small sample issues. Four to six swabs for each orifice correct this issue. It also does not provide backup if something should happen to the purple top (sometimes the top comes off in transit and it spills or it putrefies). If possible, it is advisable to collect an air-dried blood specimen on a filter or DNA paper, then place it in an envelope for later typing.

When retrieving specimens for a sexual assault kit, it is imperative to prevent cross-contamination between sites. To accomplish this, it is important to change gloves between collection sites. Swabs need to be placed carefully in each orifice without touching surrounding skin. If a swab is touched or contaminated it should be thrown away. Instruments used during the exam should only be lubricated with water.

The acquisition of a sexual assault kit is done as soon as possible after the suspected assault. It should be noted by the practitioner whether the victim bathed after the assault and the time period that has elapsed. It is preferable that the victim not bathe prior to the exam. Sexual intercourse with others should also be noted so their typing can be assessed in the mixture of DNA of the specimen. All clothing worn at the time of the assault should be confiscated for evaluation.

The smears from each of the orifices are stained by the laboratory to confirm that the collected stain contains spermatozoa and estimate the quantity of the sperm. (Image 6.3)

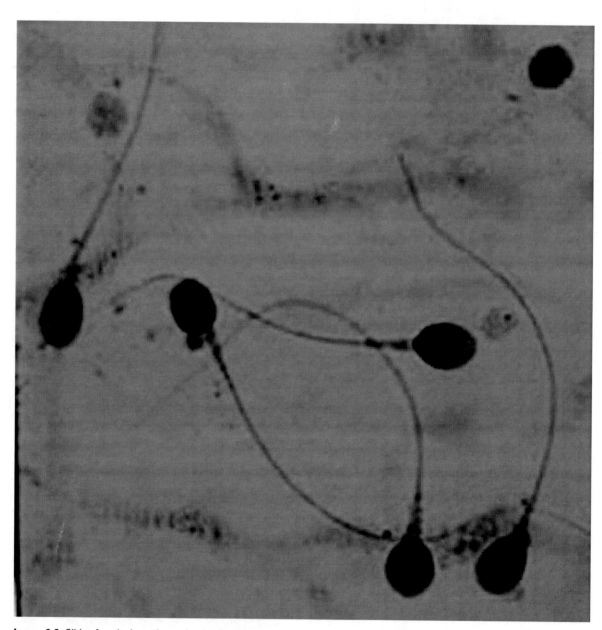

Image 6.3 Slide of vaginal specimen showing intact sperm.

A couple of case examples might illustrate some of the issues that arise:

Figure 6.1 Case Studies

Case 1 is a about young woman murdered and placed into a box freezer where she remained for 3 years. She was found nude and bound in the freezer at the residence of the male suspect. Although frozen, the body showed evidence of previous decomposition. Collection of a sexual assault kit in a frozen body was challenging. Specimens were obtained by scraping secretions from each orifice prior to total thawing. Sexual assault swabs were repeated after the body thawed. Laboratory analysis revealed 4 sperm heads from the anal orifice from the second attempt. The first kit was negative even though it had a larger sample volume. Strict glove technique was used between each orifice collection. Testimony about the collection process and attempts at getting the evidence thrown out based on contamination lasted over 4 hours. Although the number of sperm was not adequate to perform DNA (with technology available at that time), the suspect was convicted of 1st degree murder and is on death row largely because the evidence proved sexual assault (one of two charges necessary to make the suspect eligible for the death penalty). Glove and collection technique is extremely important in sexual assault collections.

Case 2 is about a young woman murdered in her residence along with two other adults. She was found nude and bound. Because of this, a sexual assault kit was obtained. The body was examined with an alternate light source (UV light) looking for additional evidence. There was a faint glistening dried stain on her thigh that did not fluoresce. It was collected anyway with the wet-dry swab technique. Subsequently, the laboratory analysis revealed a negative sexual assault kit (no sperm or fluids). The stain was positive on the thigh for semen and DNA was performed. It matched an ex-boyfriend who had been a criminalistics major (he had worn a condom to prevent detection). He was captured by a small mistake during removal of the condom. He was convicted of first degree murder and sentenced to life in prison. Collect all suspect evidence. Many times, it is irretrievable after a certain point and it is not always known at the time of collection which item will prove crucial to proving a case or in vindicating someone.

ENHANCEMENT OF SEMEN

Alternate light sources are useful to locate semen. As stated earlier, semen fluoresces under ultraviolet light. It is the secretions that fluoresce, not the presence or absence of spermatozoa.

LABORATORY TESTING OF SEMEN

The glass slides submitted with the sexual assault kit are stained with a Pap smear stain to visualize the presence of any sperm. They are identified under the microscope and a qualitative assessment is made as the quantity of the specimen.

Testing for the presence of semen depends on the quantity presented to the laboratory. Small specimen quantities require careful handling and may need to go straight to DNA analysis. Larger quantities may be evaluated via testing for acid phosphatase on the vaginal aspirate specimen. A positive value is not diagnostic of semen but presumptive of the presence of semen. Otherwise, ABO typing will be done to gain general information on the typing of the suspect. Definitive comparison is done by DNA analysis.

An Anti P-30 test is one involving the antigen antibody reaction. This test utilizes a reagent of anti-Human P-30, an antibody made in animals against human P-30. The P-30 protein is found only in human prostate secretions, which forms about 20% of the ejaculate. The suspect specimen is the antigen and in the presence of the antibody to P-30 clumps form which can be visualized on the slide and is similar to the procedure used in blood typing.

DNA testing is the standard for comparing known sperm to possible suspects. Their DNA (usually a buccal swab or blood) is compared to the banding pattern for the specimen obtained from the victim to see if there is a match.

RAPE vs. SEXUAL INTERCOURSE

Rape is a legal term and defined by state law. Statutory rape is sexual intercourse with a minor even if there is consent by the minor. Sexual intercourse implies consent by the two parties. Evidence of sexual assault does not need to include only sperm. In infants and children, the presence of venereal disease is also indicative of sexual assault. Cultures positive for gonorrhea, syphilis, venereal warts and Chlamydia from these children need be investigated thoroughly. It is important to speak to the physician for evidence of injuries and to rule out any birth canal exposure. The physician or practitioner may have used an instrument called a colposcope (a type of microscope) to visualize healed or healing injuries of the vaginal or anal areas.

Absence of sperm in a vaginal, anal or oral specimen can be due to a number of factors. It could be that the suspect wore a condom (the acid phosphatase would also be negative); that he had had a vasectomy (the acid phosphatase and the anti P-30 test would be positive). Some men have very low sperm counts (oligospermia) or ejaculation may not have occurred internally into the vagina.

SUMMARY

In this chapter the structure of spermatozoa, composition of semen, collection techniques from surfaces, live and dead victims were discussed.

DISCUSSION TOPICS

Vocabulary

- acid phosphatase
- chain of custody
- ejaculate
- semen
- secretor
- spermatozoa
- Wood's Lamp
- vasectomy
- venereal disease

DISCUSSION QUESTIONS

1. List the components of semen and where they originate.
2. Describe the parts of spermatozoa and note the location of the nucleus.
3. Discuss identification and collection of a semen stain from a porous and non-porous surface.
4. List some of the pitfalls for sexual assault kits.
5. List the contents of a sexual assault kit.

ADDITIONAL READING

Without a Trace. Advances in detecting trace evidence
   http://www.ncjrs.org/pdffiles1/jr000249b.pdf

Evidence Collection Handbook - Blood and Other Body Fluids
   http://www.firearmsid.com/KSP%20Evidence%20Manual/Biological%20Evidence.htm

Photographs courtesy of:
   http://en.wikipedia.org/wiki/Prostate
   http://en.wikipedia.org/wiki/Spermatozoa
   http://forensicservices.utah.gov/biology/

Chapter 7

Saliva, Urine, Feces

OVERVIEW

This chapter will discuss the features of saliva, urine and feces, including collection techniques and their possible contributions to an investigation.

CHAPTER OBJECTIVES

After studying this chapter, the student will be able to:
1. Understand the components of saliva, urine and feces.
2. Understand how saliva, urine and feces are evaluated as potential evidence.
3. Understand collection techniques for each of these specimen types.

HISTORICAL PERSPECTIVES

With the advent of DNA testing, saliva specimens have taken on a greater role in crime scene investigations. Multiple objects may contain saliva deposited by the offender, including cigarette butts, glasses and bottles. Saliva specimens have classically been retrieved from bite mark wounds. Urine is also a classic specimen, but for toxicological analysis.

CHARACTERISTICS OF SALIVA

Saliva is composed of mostly water and contains multiple enzymes secreted by the salivary glands. The glands are located under the tongue and in both cheeks. The purpose of saliva is to aid chewing and pulverize food. The saliva liquid softens the food aiding in its ability to be swallowed and adds enzymes, which begin the digestion of complex sugars. One of the major enzymes is called amylase. Amylase assists the digestion of starch and breaks down the sugars into smaller units. Saliva is a specimen, which may show secretor status. A secretor is a person that has their ABO blood type antigens present in body secretions and occurs in 80% of individuals. Saliva also is a source of cheek cells which can be used for DNA testing. (Image 7.1)

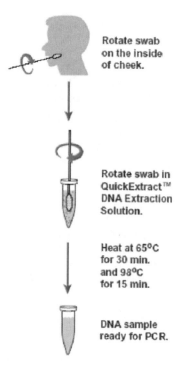

Rotate swab on the inside of cheek.

Rotate swab in QuickExtract™ DNA Extraction Solution.

Heat at 65°C for 30 min. and 98°C for 15 min.

DNA sample ready for PCR.

Image 7.1 Procedure for obtaining DNA using Catch-All™ device and QuickExtract™ Solution. Reprinted with permission from www.epicentre.com.

COLLECTION OF BUCCAL SMEARS

In 1990, with the advent of CODIS (the FBI's computerized Combined DNA Index System), state laws mandated the collection of DNA from convicted offenders of sexual assault and certain other felonies determined by each state. The National DNA Index System contains electronically stored information from two sources: the offenders and from the crime scene. The DNA from both can be compared to solve 'cold cases', link unsolved crimes that have occurred across state lines or jurisdictions. This allows crimes to be linked that otherwise would have no other means to be compared. All 50 states participate in the National DNA Index System except Mississippi. As of June 2004, 1.77 million offender profiles and over 85,000 crime scene profiles have been added to the database. Over 18,000 investigations have been aided by this data.[1] Procurement of the offender data is obtained prior to their release. This has been one of the ethical debates of the system as to when to obtain the DNA sample. Should it be obtained at the time of the arrest, time of conviction, after all appeals, or just prior to release? Swabbing or scraping the inner cheek obtains the specimen. Doing so harvests a sample of nucleated cells and is called a buccal smear. (Images 7.2 & 7.3)

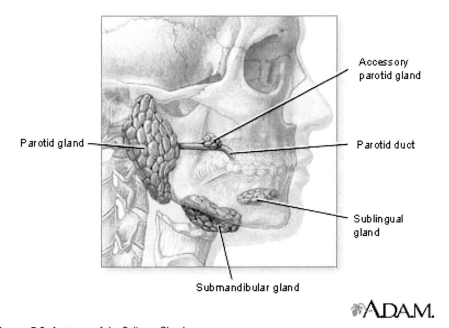

Image 7.2 Anatomy of the Salivary Glands.

Image 7.3 Obtaining a buccal smear from the inner cheek.

Photo permission by
Bode Technology Group, Inc.
www.bodetech.com

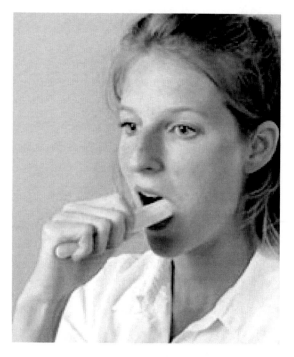

This collection technique has advantages over drawing a blood specimen for DNA as it is non-invasive, requires little training in collection techniques and once the buccal smear is collected and dried properly it is easily stored. Different types of kits are available for collection. Some are like tongue blades with adherent paper; others are like swabs or small brushes to scrape and harvest the needed cells. (Images 7.4 & 7.5)

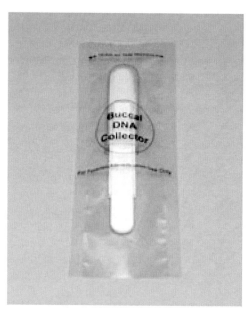

Image 7.4 Buccal DNA collection device.

Photo permission by
Bode Technology Group, Inc.
www.bodetech.com

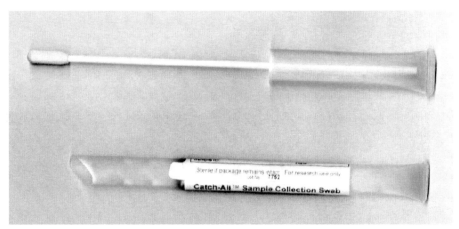

Image 7.5 Buccal DNA procurement device. Catch-All™ is a porous swab found to give greater DNA yields over conventional brush or swab techniques. Reprinted with permission from www.epicentre.com/ ©EPICENTER Technologies Corporation. All rights reserved.

At the time of testing, the cells are easily hydrated and resuspended in a solution to be amplified and tested using PCR technology. Because of the large number of anticipated samples in the future, automation of the DNA profile on these swabs is anticipated.

COLLECTING SALIVA AT A SCENE

Saliva collection depends on the volume of specimen present and can be done via the buccal swab technique described above. This is preferred over saliva into a cup for testing of a possible offender. If a measurable quantity of unknown fluid, possibly saliva, exists, it can be collected into a sterile specimen cup (although usually a sample of the material is adequate). If it is a small amount, but wet, it can be absorbed onto a filter paper or small piece of cloth. Sometimes the specimen is very small but still wet; it can be absorbed onto a dry swab. If the specimen is dry, the swab can be dampened with distilled water and rolled over the surface. A second dry swab can be used to absorb any remainder of the specimen. The latter technique is the one used to collect specimens from bite marks on skin.

It should be remembered that many objects may contain adherent saliva from which DNA may be obtained. These include saliva on a cup, glass or bottle, cigarette butts, bite marks, gum, envelopes and some stamps. The mouth has abundant bacteria so it is imperative that collected specimens be dried thoroughly or frozen to preserve their integrity.

ENHANCEMENT OF SALIVA

Saliva, like other body secretions such as semen, fluoresces under alternate light sources depending on the wavelength used. This may assist in the location of saliva evidence.

Figure 7.1 Case Study

The following is a case study of the importance of considering saliva specimens for collection as evidence[2]:

In Austin, Texas, an investigator knowledgeable about DNA technology was able to solve the rape of a local college student. Having read about the potential for obtaining DNA evidence from the ligature used to strangle a victim, the investigator requested DNA testing on the phone cord used to choke the victim in his case. He realized that in the course of choking someone, enough force and friction is applied to the rope or cord that the perpetrator's skin cells may rub off his hands and be left on the ligature. The investigator's request paid off in an unanticipated way. In spite of the attacker's attempt to avoid identification through DNA evidence by wearing both a condom and rubber gloves, a reliable DNA profile was developed from the evidence. During the struggle, the attacker was forced to use one hand to hold the victim down, leaving only one hand to pull the phone cord tight. The attacker had to grab the remaining end of the cord with his mouth, thereby depositing his saliva on the cord. Although the developed profile came from saliva rather than skin, DNA not only solved the case in Austin, but also linked the perpetrator to a similar sexual assault in Waco.

CHARACTERISTICS OF FECES

Feces are composed of undigested food material, usually fibers and complex substances, which cannot be broken down and absorbed. As it passes through the digestive tract and out through the rectum a few adherent epithelial cells may become attached. However, feces are not usually a first specimen of choice in the analysis tree. Usually other specimens are just as productive in analysis of DNA data and are easier to work with.

One exception where feces may prove useful in analysis is in the newborn. Their initial fecal specimens are called meconium and reflect the maternal environment during the fetal gestation. For this reason, meconium specimens are useful for toxicologic analysis for illicit drug use during the pregnancy. Meconium has the appearance of thick, sticky, dark brown material and is usually passed for the first 2 to 3 days following delivery. In an unborn fetus, it can be collected during the autopsy from the gastrointestinal tract.

COLLECTING FECES AT A SCENE

In those cases where a possible smear of feces needs to be collected, it can be obtained with a distilled water dampened swab then dried prior to placing it in a collection envelope. Rarely would a large specimen need to be collected, but if need be, it could be placed in a sterile cup container.

Meconium from a newborn is not usually a large specimen and can be scooped and placed inside an opened vacuum blood drawing tube or placed into a sterile cup container. Swabs are not usually helpful in toxicologic analysis.

CHARACTERISTICS OF URINE

Urine is composed largely of water and water-soluble materials that are in excess in the blood. Urine is created by the kidneys through filtration of the blood through a complex gradient principle. The blood is filtered across a structure called the glomerulus within a structure called the nephron (thousands of these make up each kidney). Then materials are reabsorbed across the nephron membrane to maintain the balance of key elements in the blood (sodium, potassium, chloride) and excrete the byproducts of protein metabolism. The cells lining the nephron and the collecting system through the bladder are called transitional cells. These, white cells and other nucleated material may be excreted with the urine and may be recovered for DNA evaluation.

Urine is a great screening material for drug analysis. It is easy for the drug screening instruments to work with urine by using antibody to antigen methods. This is discussed further in the toxicology chapter.

COLLECTING URINE

Urine is most easily collected in a sterile cup container. During an autopsy, samples of the total volume may be collected into 2 or 3 vacuum specimen tubes. If the specimen is to be used for toxicology purposes, it should be collected in grey tubes containing sodium fluoride. If the specimen is to be used for serology or DNA purposes, it would be best to collect it in a plain red top without preservative or into a purple top (check with your laboratory for their preference). Urine, like other secretions fluoresces with alternate light sources.

SUMMARY

This chapter discussed the anatomy of the salivary gland and basic kidney structure. Collection techniques for saliva, urine and feces were discussed as well as their usefulness in a crime scene investigation.

DISCUSSION TOPICS

Vocabulary

- amylase
- saliva
- feces
- meconium
- glomerulus
- nephron
- urine
- transitional cells
- Buccal Smear
- CODIS
- NDIS

DISCUSSION QUESTIONS

1. List the components of saliva and the role each play.

2. List multiple areas where salvia might be recovered at a crime scene.

3. What are CODIS and NDIS?

4. How is saliva collected from convicted felons for entry into the national data bank?

5. What is meconium and how can it be used for toxicology purposes?

6. What is urine and how can it be used for toxicology purposes?

ADDITIONAL READING

Buccal Collection Procedures
    http://www.epicentre.com/pdfforum/8_2buccal.pdf
    http://www.epicentre.com/item.asp?id=270#RelatedProducts
    http://www.bodetech.com/services/buccal_overview.html
    The Flash demo explains Buccal DNA collection

ENDNOTES

1. http://www.fbi.gov/hq/lab/codis/program.htm
2. http://www.ncjrs.org/txtfiles1/nij/194197.txt

Chapter 8

Hair and Fingernails

OVERVIEW

In this chapter, the anatomy of hair and fingernails will be discussed. Collection and analysis techniques will be reviewed as well as images of each.

CHAPTER OBJECTIVES

After studying this chapter, the student will be able to:
1. Understand the anatomy of a hair and hair follicle.
2. View different images of hairs from human and non-human sources.
3. Understand collection techniques for hair and fingernails.
4. Understand the anatomy of a fingernail.
5. Laboratory techniques for hair and fingernail analysis.

HISTORICAL PERSPECTIVES

It is unclear, but Galileo may have been the inventor of a primitive microscope as early as 1609. Some of the first microscopes, as we know them today, were invented in the mid1800s but it wasn't until Sir Sydney Smith, one of the original forensic examiners working in the early 1900-1930s utilized a comparison microscope to solve a crime. Smith compared hairs and fibers left on a gunny sack with samples from the the suspect. It was in the 1960s that the comparison microscope came into more widespread use as a forensic tool in fiber, hair, and ballistic comparison.

CHARACTERISTICS OF HAIR

Anatomy of a Hair

Hairs are composed largely of keratin as an outgrowth of the skin. Keratin is similar to a flake of skin or a scale. Human hair varies in its appearance over the body, e.g., head hair, pubic hair, arm and eyebrow hairs all have similar characteristics of a shaft and cuticle but their appearance under the microscope will vary even in the same individual. A classic example is differentiating head hair and pubic hair. Head hair is often dyed, and may be straight or curly. Pubic hair usually contains the native color and is most times curly.

Hairs normally grow about 1 cm per month and cycle through a period of growth and a period of quiescence. The growth phase of hair is referred to as the anagen phase; hairs forcibly removed or pulled during this stage will appear stretched out at the root and have attached cells from the cells within the hair follicle (Images 8.1 & 8.2).

Image 8.1 Forcibly removed or pulled hair.

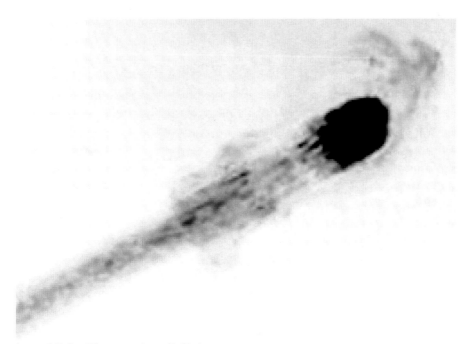

Image 8.2 Forcibly removed or pulled hair.

The quiescent or resting phase is called the telogen phase. This is when hairs may naturally fall out and will exhibit a blunt or club shaped root without tissue attached (Image 8.3). Since the hair is made of cells, it does contain DNA within the keratin as do the cells at the root.

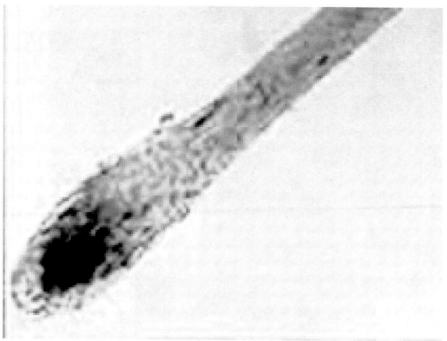

Image 8.3 Naturally shed hair.

A hair is composed of a shaft and a root, which reside in a follicle of the skin (Image 8.4). The shaft of the hair is the portion seen as hair and is composed of dead keratin cells, melanin and metals absorbed from the environment or deposited during its growth. The root lies within the skin and at the base is the papilla the only portion that is growing.

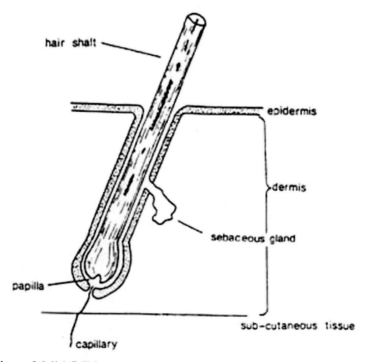

Image 8.4 Hair Follicle

The internal structures of a hair include the cuticle, medulla and cortex (Image 8.5). The cuticle region is the outermost and forms a horny type layer of keratin cells, cuticle scales. The medulla is the center core (Image 8.6). The cortex is the area between and contains the pigment granules and ovoid bodies (Image 8.7). Pigment granules are what give the hair its color, are composed of melanin granules and vary in amount and distribution in different races and color of hair. Ovoid bodies are unknown in their origin but also provide a useful characteristic to differentiate hairs.

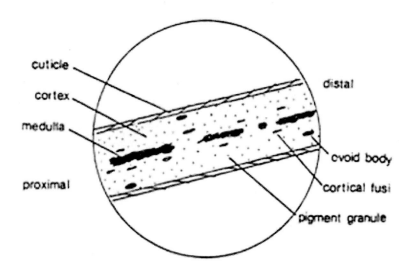

Image 8.5 Structure of a hair used to categorize it.

Image 8.6 Three basic medullary types found in human hairs: Trace (top), Discontinuous (middle), or Continuous (bottom)

Human vs. Non-human hair

Each animal, including humans has characteristic appearances of length, color, shape, root structure, and internal characteristics that allow them to be classified and identified (Figures 8.7, 8.7.1, 8.8, 8.1, 9, 9.1, 10, 11, 11.1).

Image 8.7 Cortex Pigment. Granulation in a human hair. Note the concentration of the pigment is toward the cuticle edge and not in the medullary portion as is seen in animals.

Image 8.8 Dog Hair Shaft

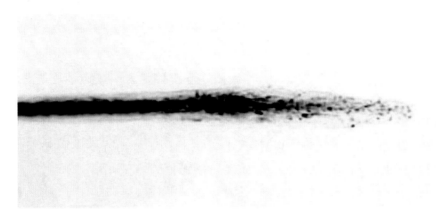

Image 8.8.1 Dog Hair Root

Image 8.9 Cat Hair Shaft

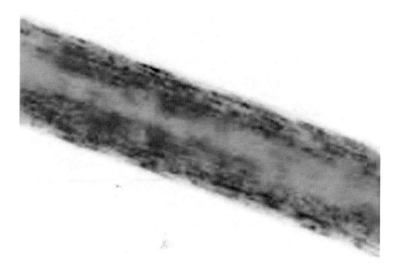

Image 10 Caucasian Hair

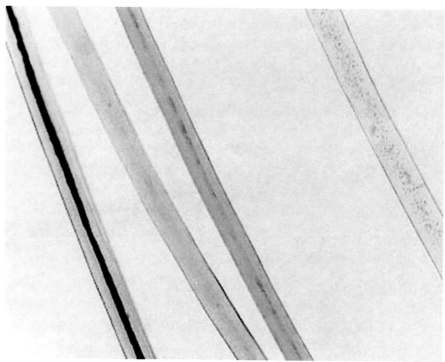

Image 8.10.1 Hairs from Caucasian Decent

Image 8.11 Hair from Mongoloid or Asian decent

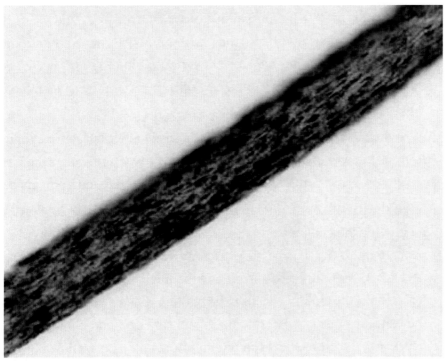

Image 8.12 Negroid Hair

Image 8.12.1 Hairs from Negroid decent

COLLECTING HAIR AT A SCENE

The importance of a hair is the possible link of physical contact between the suspect and the victim. Whenever there is contact between two people there is the possibility of transfer of hairs and fibers. The uniqueness and the number of the transfer will determine how strong the link is. Sometimes the transfer occurs onto clothing left at the scene, either worn by the suspect or as part of something they came in contact with, such as bed sheets or carpeting.

When collecting a hair sample off a surface like a floor or counter, it is easiest to pick it up with a pair of forceps (tweezers) and place it in an envelope correctly marked with the location and demographic data.

If the hairs are adherent to a sheet or piece of clothing, it is easiest to gently fold the cloth inward into a small bundle and place it into a brown paper bag. If it is necessary to remove the clothing (e.g., from a decedent), it would be best to collect the trace prior to removal so that it isn't lost. If the clothing needs to be photographed prior to placing it into the bag, it can be gently laid out on a clean sheet and photographed. If necessary, the clean sheet can be submitted to the lab or fallen evidence can be collected from the sheet.

Large areas that may contain adherent trace evidence such as hair and fibers can be vacuumed and the collection bag submitted to the laboratory for analysis.

If exemplar hairs need to be collected from a victim or suspect, the hairs need to be removed by plucking rather than cutting. This ensures the hair root is obtained and can be used as part of the identification process. The FBI recommends at least 25 hairs from each body area need to be collected for adequate sampling; others recommend 50 hairs. Because hair over a surface like the head can vary in length, color and appearance, at least 5 sites need to be sampled. The plucked hairs are placed into a clean envelope and marked appropriately.

All sexual assault kits need to be submitted with known exemplars of the victim. This allows the lab to sort the known source of recovered hairs from those coming from an unknown suspect. The same evidence technique needs to be utilized after recovering hairs from a scene. If a known victim or pet are known to have been present, hairs from them should be obtained as known examples to sort out the unknowns.

LABORATORY EVALUATION OF HAIR

Image 8.13 Human Hair Shaft

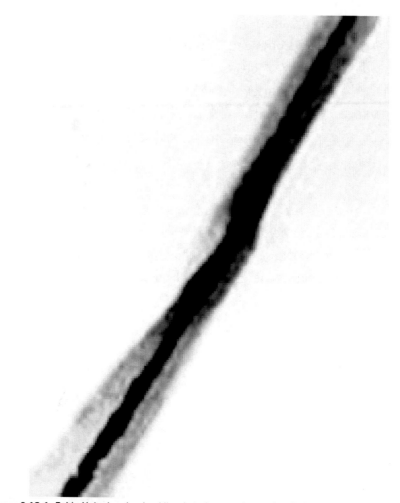

Image 8.13.1 Pubic Hair showing buckling (wiry) or curving to the shaft

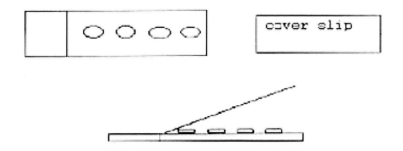

Image 8.14 How to prepare a slide for examination of hair samples and other microscopic materials

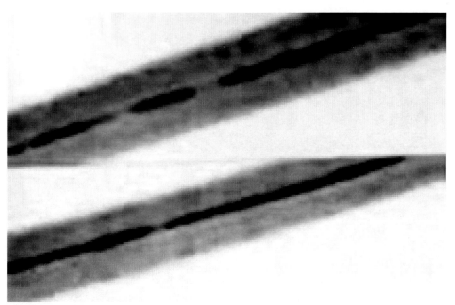

Image 8.15 Hair match with comparison microscope

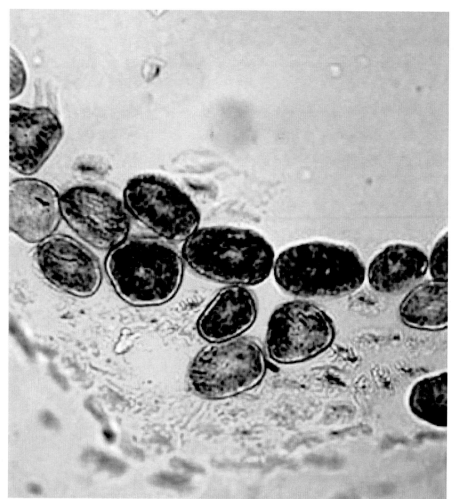

Image 8.16 Cross-section of Caucasian hair

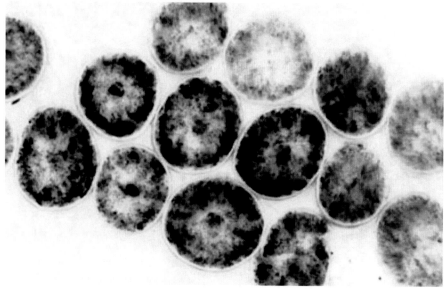

Image 8.17 Cross-section of Mongoloid Hair

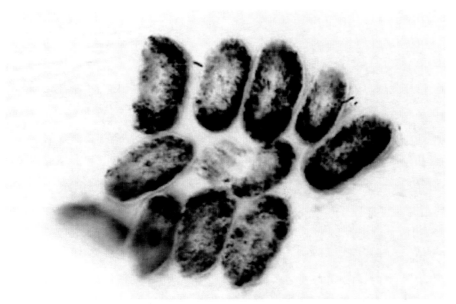

Image 8.18 Cross-section of Negroid Hairs

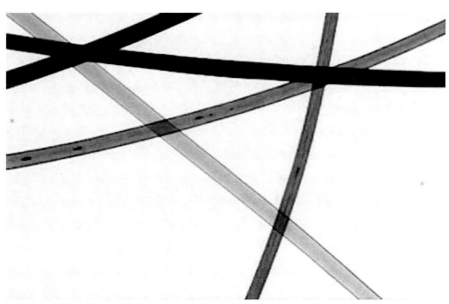

Image 8.19 Dyed Human Hair

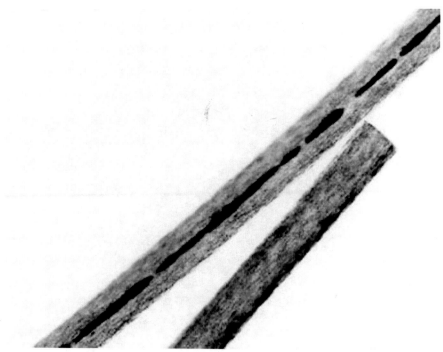

Image 8.20 Cut human hair

Image 8.21 Broken human hair

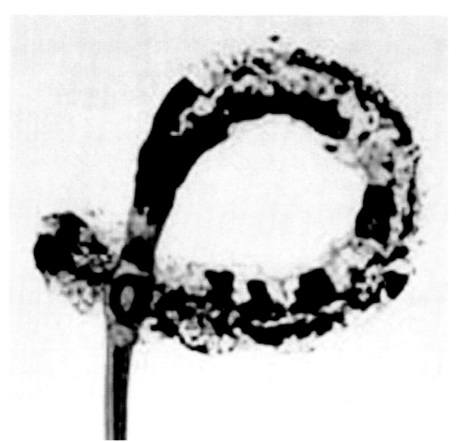

Image 8.22 Hair affected by burning

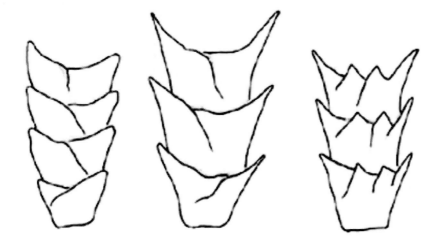

Image 8.23 Example of non-human scales

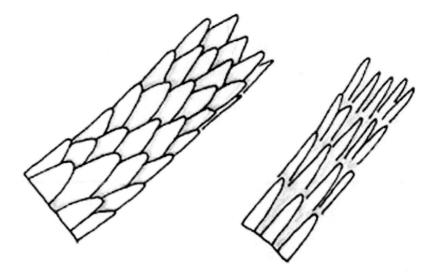

Image 8.24   Example of non-human scales

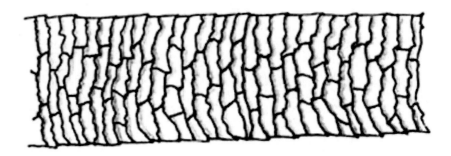

Image 8.25   Example of human scales

Image 8.26 Human hair root

Image 8.27 Pigment animal hair

The two most common body areas evaluated are head hairs and pubic hairs (Images 8.13 & 8.13.1). Hairs are evaluated by preparing a glass slide of the hair (Image 8.14) and evaluating it under a light microscope. To compare it to a known hair, a comparison microscope can be used. This microscope places two specimens on separate microscope stages to view them through a single eyepiece simultaneously (Image 8.15). This allows side-by-side comparison of two specimens to determine a match between the unknown sample and a suspect or elimination sample (person known to be related to the scene, e.g., victim or person known to live in a residence).

Evaluation of Race

Evaluating a hair for racial characteristics include looking at the hair under the microscope for the distribution of pigment along the hair shaft, the appearance of buckling and the diameter of the hair on cross-section.

Caucasian hairs have patchy, fine pigment granules, are fine to medium thickness and on cross-section appear round to oval (Image 8.16). Hairs of Mongoloid or Asian descent are thicker than Caucasian, have grouped thick pigment granules, coarse thickness, and are circular on cross section (Image 8.17). Hairs of African descent have large pigment granules arranged in clumps, tend to be wavy or curled and are flat on cross-section (Image 8.18).

Generally, reports read as consistent with a known sample, inconsistent with a known sample or inconclusive results.

Altered Hair Characteristics

Scalp hair can be easily altered using dyes and multiple colors may be evident throughout the length of the hair (Image 8.19). Other alterations are cut hair ends (Image 8.20), broken hair ends (Image 8.21) and burning artifacts (Image 8.22).

DNA EVALUATION OF HAIR

Keratin present in hair is a tough material. To release the DNA from the interior of the cells, the keratin cell membrane must be broken down (called digestion) and this is done by heating and an enzyme (proteinase K), which releases the DNA[1]. DNA is present throughout the length of the hair and in the root. In some cases, the root may have attached scalp cells if it was forcibly removed and this can be a source of nuclear DNA. It is possible to do nuclear DNA typing on a single hair however, practically it may be difficult because it may be of poor quality of the DNA present (shed hair is all dead cells) and the nuclear DNA is present in small amounts. Adherent DNA to the surface of the hair (fingerprint) may obscure the typing of the hair itself. PCR technology is helpful in amplifying small amounts of DNA but if contaminated, the target DNA desired may be overshadowed. Mitochondrial DNA techniques may be necessary. The big advantage of mitochondrial DNA is the larger number of copies per cell and the circular structure of mitochondrial DNA make it more resistant to degradation.

CHARACTERISTICS OF FINGERNAILS

Anatomy of a Fingernail

Fingernails are made of keratin like hair or skin but grow in flat sheets. The exposed portion that is visualized is called the nail body and is attached at the base by the nail root. The body serves to protect the sensitive underlying skin and convey touch and pain sensations to the sensors in the root area. To grow from the cuticle to the tip takes approximately 5 to 6 months. Male nails tend to be thicker than females and grow faster than females. Each fingernail of the hands grows at a different rate; the middle finger grows the fastest and the little and thumb grows the slowest. Nails grow fastest on the dominant hand and nail growth is not affected by supplements or vitamin intake in well-nourished individuals.[2]

Nails contain longitudinal ridges both on the exterior and under surfaces that are thought to be characteristic for each individual and are created by skin ridges under the nail, much like fingerprint ridges. As the nail grows, it acquires the ridges from the skin below it[3]. These are compared using an electron microscope of a cross section of the nail in question and comparing it to the subjects corresponding nail.

Perhaps more useful is analysis of adherent nail polish and comparing it to the exemplar. Portions of acrylic nails can also be compared to a subject's nail. Broken nails can be placed next to the possible source to identify a match.

COLLECTING FINGERNAILS

If fragments of fingernails are found at a scene, they can be collected into a filter paper or placed directly into an envelope. Fragments can be matched to a victim or suspect.

The material under the nails is perhaps of greater evidentiary value. If skin or blood is present, it can be gently scraped into a filter paper using the nail file portion of a clean pair of nail clippers, a clean toothpick or a swab stick. Use one for each hand. A slightly moistened swab can also be used to swipe under the nails for collection of the needed cells (one for each hand). The swabs are air dried then placed into an envelope, correctly labeled for the proper hand, along with the date, case and demographic data. Fingernail scrapings are folded into a filter paper and placed into an envelope with the labeling information. Very little DNA needs to be recovered to use the PCR techniques available today to analyze DNA. It is important to recover the material under the nails with as little trauma and bleeding as possible because the victim's DNA may overwhelm the small amount present under the nail from the Suspect.

SUMMARY

In this chapter the anatomy and structure of hairs were reviewed to identify the components used to make scientific comparisons. Collection techniques and laboratory analysis were also discussed.

DISCUSSION TOPICS

Vocabulary

- anagen phase
- telogen phase
- cortex
- medulla
- cuticle
- keratin
- ovoid bodies
- pigment granules
- scales
- comparison microscope

REVIEW QUESTIONS

1. What is a hair follicle? Name the major parts.
2. Name the layers of a hair used to differentiate it from non-human sources.
3. Name the layers of a hair used to characterize it.
4. List the major characteristics of a hair of Caucasian descent.
5. List the major characteristics of a hair of Mongoloid or Asian descent.
6. List the major characteristics of a hair of African descent.
7. Discuss problems associated with performing DNA on a single hair recovered from a scene.
8. What are the anagen and telogen phases of a hair?
9. Discuss the different types of collection techniques to recover hair from a scene.
10. Discuss the laboratory evaluation of a broken nail recovered from a scene.

ADDITIONAL READING

Hairs, Fibers, Crime and Evidence
www.fbi.gov/hq/lab/fsc/backissu/july2000/deedric1.htm

Microscopy of Hair Part II, A Practical Guide and Manual for Animal Hair, Forensic Science Communications, July 2004, Vol. 6 No. 3
www.fbi.gov/hq/lab/fsc/current/research/2004_03_research02.htm#structure

Microscopy of Hair Part 1: A Practical Guide and Manual for Human Hairs by Douglas W. Deedrick, Forensic Science Communications January 2004 – Volume 6 – Number 1
www.fbi.gov/hq/lab/fsc/backissu/jan2004/research/2004_01_research01b.htm

Mythos Anatomy of a Fingernail
www.mythos.com/webmd/Content.aspx?P=NAILS1&E=14

ENDNOTES

1. www.promega.com/profiles/502/ProfilesInDNA_502_11.pdf

2. www.mythos.com/webmd/Content.aspx?P=NAILS1&E=14

3. *Comparison of Fingernail Striation Patterns in Identical Twins,* J. B. Kempton et.al. Journal of Forensic Sciences, Vol. 37, No. 6, November 1992, pp. 1534-1540).

Chapter 9

Toxicology, Entomology, Botany, Uncollectible Evidence

OVERVIEW

This chapter includes toxicology (testing for drugs), entomology (study of insects), botany (study of plants), and how they can relate to crimes and crime scenes. At the end of the chapter, documentation of injuries will be discussed, how patterned injuries can give an indication of the type of instrument used in a crime and how to document them accurately.

CHAPTER OBJECTIVES

After studying this chapter, the student will be able to:
1. Gain basic understanding of the science of toxicology.
2. Identify toxicology specimens and understand proper collection techniques.
3. Gain understanding of proper transport and handling of toxicology specimens.
4. Gain a basic understanding of the science of forensic entomology.
5. Identify useful forensic entomology specimens, proper collection, and transport techniques.
6. Identify useful forensic botanical specimens, proper collection, and transport techniques.
7. Identify injuries and use proper terminology to describe the different types of injuries.
8. Understand the proper basic photographic techniques used to document injuries.
9. Recognize basic patterned injuries and proper photographic techniques used to document these injuries.

HISTORICAL PERSPECTIVES

Forensic toxicology was the earliest forensic science and is related to the history of poisons throughout the ages. Arsenic, strychnine, cyanide, etc., are included in the category of poisons as the definition can include any substance when it is ingested in toxic amounts. This implies a homicidal nature and a crime. However, toxicology has equal importance in determining suicidal and accidental causes of death.

The history of forensic entomology is an interesting one. The basis for studying the development of insects in rotting meat began in the mid 1600s when they learned that rotting meat did not spontaneously emit maggots but that they resulted from flies. In the late 1800s, a Frenchman named J.P. Megnin, hypothesized that entomology could be useful in solving crimes. Probably the most interesting notation regarding forensic entomology is the one of an ancient Chinese 'death investigator' from 1200 AD. A murder was committed in a rural village by slashing with a sickle. After questioning many of the villagers to no avail, the investigator had each of the farmers bring their sickle to the town square and lay them out. Flies were attracted to only one sickle; the farmer then confessed to the crime[1].

Forensic botany is a relatively new addition to the forensic sciences. The first citing of botany being utilized is thought to be in the Lindberg kidnapping of the 1920s. A fragment of wood from the ladder used in the kidnapping was compared and matched to pieces of wood used to make the ladder. This information was linked to lumber mills with the wood. Eventually, Bruno Hauptman, a carpenter, was apprehended and convicted.

TOXICOLOGY

Toxicology is the study of chemicals and drugs in the body. Ingested drugs are chemicals that sometimes react in the form they are ingested in (parent compound), and other times are metabolized (called metabolites) to their active form. Testing methods target identification of both the parent compound and their major metabolites. The rate of breakdown of the parent compound into its metabolites, their appearances in the different specimen types, including excretion from the body, may indicate how long ago a drug was introduced into the body.

Blood

Blood specimens are typically the standard for quantification of a substance and its effect on the body at any point in time. There are three major areas that forensic medicine concentrates its efforts in detecting: alcohol, illicit drugs and prescription drugs.

Blood Alcohol

Ethanol, the active component of alcoholic beverages, is tested for in whole blood. Many states have established a legal limit of intoxication of 0.08 mg/dl, while others have a legal limit of 1.0 mg/dl. It has been found that at this level, a person will have impaired judgment and reaction time.

Gas chromatography testing determines blood alcohol levels. Other alcohols can be ingested and may be suspected in overdoses and accidental poisonings. These include methanol ethylene glycol (common in antifreeze compounds) and isopropyl alcohol (rubbing alcohol). Other volatile compounds like gasoline, paint thinners, diesel etc. are analyzed utilizing gas chromatography.

Urine specimens are usually screened for illicit prescription drugs. For suspected categories, the absolute presence or absence can be determined by using gas chromatography-mass spectrophotometry methods (GC-MS).

Gas chromatography is a method to separate samples using a mobile and stationary phase. The sample is injected in the instrument and turned into a gas. The mobile phase carries the gas through the stationary phase (called a column). The gas separates into its different components based on their ability to flow through the column over time (called retention time). The retention time is characteristic for each compound and can be identified by comparison of the retention time spectrum to a library (in a computer). The mass spectrophotometer is usually attached to the GC and adds information about the mass and charge of the different components being screened for.

Urine

Urine typically is a point of excretion for toxicologic substances. Quantification of drug amounts in this sample is typically not very helpful because the urine concentrates these products during the excretion process. The advantage of urine specimens is their ability to be easily screened with instrumentation and because they can reflect excretion byproducts that were ingested some time ago. For example, a urine drug screen can remain positive for byproducts of marijuana use for up to 30 days.

Urine drug screens are usually done by an antibody-antigen reaction. These can be cross-reactive between different drug compounds, leading to false positives. Because of this, urine drug screens, which are positive for a substance, need to be confirmed with a blood screen for that substance using the GC-MS, which is more specific.

Bile

Bile is a green, viscous liquid excreted by the liver and normally aids in the digestion of fatty foods. Some drugs are metabolized in the liver into their byproducts and are detectable in the bile fluid. In these substances, bile is similar to urine in that these products get metabolized and excreted in the bile through the digestive tract. The only time this specimen is available is in autopsied bodies. It is used in those cases where a drug may be primarily excreted by the liver, but is not used as a primary testing fluid. It is also useful as a genetic screening tool in babies suspected of dying of certain fatty liver diseases.

Tissue

Tissue used for toxicology sampling is usually only available through autopsied bodies. Tissues to be retrieved include the liver and brain. In recent years, brain tissue has been tested to monitor the effects of drugs on the brain. People's actions prior to death are a result of their brain function. High levels of drugs "seen by the brain" may give us a better understanding of drug effects than blood. An example is an excited delirium associated with cocaine or methamphetamine intoxication. This excited delirium has been associated with police-in-custody deaths. The values of the drugs can give us information about the drugs and resulting actions by the prisoner. Tissues are especially sought after in aircraft accidents as many of these decedents have little bodily fluids to collect. The FAA provides a special toxicology collection kit for the tissues they would like submitted on the pilot and copilot in any aircraft crash where they are decedents.

Hair

The classic example of using hair in toxicology is for arsenic testing. Arsenic is excreted by the kidneys but if ingested faster than it can be excreted, it accumulates in the hair and nails. Because of this, arsenic can be detected in embalmed bodies and those buried for an extensive period of time.

Gastric Contents and Feces

Gastric contents are materials recently ingested by mouth. This can include food material, pill fragments, foreign bodies etc. Gastric contents can be collected in the living or dead. In the live patient of suspected overdose, a large diameter tube is inserted into the mouth to the stomach to remove unabsorbed pills and to insert a charcoal, which neutralizes many drugs that are ingested. The gastric contents can then be analyzed to determine the etiology of the ingestion. In decedents, the contents are examined for the presence of pills, the quantity and the type and to aid in determining the possible cause of death. This material cannot only be used to identify the substance but can be quantified as an aid in determining the manner of death; suicide or accident. Identifying large quantities of pill residue/fragments is more consistent with suicide than an accidental overdose.

Gastric contents are sometimes examined to aid in the time of death. Gastric emptying varies greatly between individuals and depends on the type of food eaten. Generally, it takes 4 to 6 hours for a meal to be digested and leave the stomach. In some cases, the food particles can be identified and compared to the food last known to be ingested. An example is the following scenario:

A child was abducted from a local restaurant and known to have eaten a hamburger and French fries. He was found two weeks later decomposing in the desert. Autopsy revealed hot dog fragments. This would indicate that the child had been fed sometime after the abduction and was not killed immediately. If however, hamburger and French fries were discovered, then the child was killed in closer proximity to the ingestion of that food, or was given a similar meal after the abduction.

Usually, some specimen other than feces is available for toxicology testing. However, in a fetus or infant, blood volumes are very small and urine may not be present. Fecal samples can be useful in the evaluation of whether drugs were a factor in the demise of the fetus or infant. In utero, the feces (called meconium) is concentrated over the length of the pregnancy and can be used to evaluate for maternal drug use during the gestation. Meconium is usually passed for the first 3 days or so after a live birth. Toxicology testing may aid in determining the answer to maternal drug use in the live birth or in the death of the fetus/infant.

Vitreous

Vitreous fluid is the liquid retrieved from the interior of the eyes and is only available in decedents. It is a thick clear viscous fluid, which is protected from blood penetration or contamination. It is characterized by a lag period from the levels seen in blood. This is especially useful in alcohol metabolism and can give an indication if the person is on the way up or down from a particular blood value.

It is also useful in evaluation of blood electrolytes such as sodium, glucose and creatinine in decedents. With death, blood begins to deteriorate immediately and these values can be difficult to evaluate. Vitreous is protected somewhat from the deterioration because of its location within the eye and can be used to evaluate for dehydration and diabetes mellitus.

ENTOMOLOGY

Forensic entomology is defined as the study of insects as they relate to legal matters. This can encompass insects in food or grain products, insects in structures or buildings, or insects as they relate to medicine. Forensic entomologists are asked to estimate the postmortem interval or whether the body has been moved. Insects can also serve as a medium for toxicology.

Life Cycle

Upon death (even before death in some circumstances), insects will attack the body. Notorious for this are roaches, ants and flies. The types of insects and the order in which they attack the body is determined partly by opportunity through exposure of the body to environmental conditions. Insects have life cycles just like other organisms. The life cycle and number of days to attain the different stages is the basis for estimating the time of death. To understand this, it is important to discuss the life cycles of common insects which prey upon a body, so that the proper specimens can be obtained for study.

Two common flies involved in forensic investigations are the blow flies (Family: Calliphoridae) and the flesh flies (Family: Sarcophagidai). Both have the same basic life cycle for larvae (instar I, instar II, instar III), pupae, and adult. (Figure 9.1) When collecting specimens for submission to a forensic entomologist, it is important to collect a sampling of each of the different life stages that are seen on and around the body. Two types of samples are collected, 1) in a preservative and 2) live samples. The preservative stops the time line and preserves the insect stage when the body is discovered. The live samples allow the entomologist to raise the larval form to adulthood to study the life cycle of that insect type. Experimentally, they are raised under similar environmental conditions. This is used to estimate the time frame required for it to have developed in the body. Some insects are also present only at certain times of the year so that too may give an indication of the length of time a body has been there. In buried bodies, beetles and similar underground insects need to be collected for study, including their eggs, larvae, pupae and adult forms.

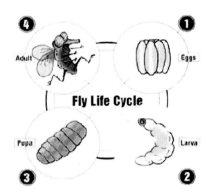

Figure 9.1 Fly Life Cycle

The preservative used to collect insects is 50% isopropyl alcohol. Those collected live can be placed in a damp paper towel in a cup. If the transit time is long, a small amount of sawdust in the bottom of the cup with a small amount of raw meat added will allow them to feed. Adult fly specimens are not critical for timing as they just indicate the species; however, a few need to be collected to aid the identification. Each specimen cup needs to be labeled with the location of the collection site, case number, date and time of collection.

Toxicology

In decomposed bodies, the fluids and many of the tissues normally used for toxicology may not be available or be usable. Toxicology is an important step in determining cause of death and many times gives clues for circumstances surrounding the death in suicides and homicides. Because maggots feed on the tissues, they ingest substances present in the body including drugs. Maggots can be collected and blended to make slurry, then strained and analyzed for the presence of illicit drugs. Quantification is not possible, but the presence or absence of a drug (qualification) can be determined. In this instance, the maggots are collected in a specimen jar without preservative or feeding material. The lab will prepare the specimen as needed.

BOTANY

Forensic botany is the study of plants in relationship to crime. This can range from studying seedpods, to seasonal variation of plants and estimating the time a body has been present in a location.

Forensic Applications

Plants or seedpods found under a body may give a clue as to when it was placed there. Some plants exhibit seasonal variation and this information can be determined by a forensic botanist. Botanists can also assist in identifying seedpods and their origin. Tree products such as seedpods have DNA that can be sequenced and matched to the tree that produced it. A case that comes to mind is a palo verde seedpod recovered from the back of a pickup truck belonging to a suspect. The associated body was found near a palo verde tree. The forensic botanist matched the DNA from the seedpod to the DNA from the palo verde tree. Other palo verde trees were compared and their DNA sequence was found to be different from the suspect tree. This evidence was used to convict the suspect.

UNCOLLECTIBLE EVIDENCE

Definitions of the Types of Injuries

The following terms are used to define the various injuries (abrasion, contusion, laceration, incision, or fracture), which can all be patterned

Abrasion

A common term for abrasion is "scrape." It is caused by friction of an object sliding across the skin, or the skin sliding across an object. An example is "road rash" where the skin has slid across the surface of the road. The friction causes the loss of the surface layers of the skin and the resulting redness. Another common example is a carpet burn.

Contusion

The common term for contusion is "bruise." It is caused by a force being applied to the surface of the skin, causing rupture of the underlying, small blood vessels (capillaries). This rupture causes bleeding into the fat and connective tissue of the underlying skin. Bruises go through a series of color changes throughout the healing process. In general, it goes from blue/pink to green/yellow to brown and resolution. The rate of this color change varies from person to person, the amount of clothing and padding in the skin and the person's underlying health. The specific timing of an injury is not able to be determined to an exact day or hour, however, in one individual, biopsies from different sites can be used to estimate their relative time of injury to one another and their stage of healing. The physiology of the healing of a bruise involves the breakdown of the hemoglobin in the red cells and its reabsorption by the body. This type of analysis requires actual tissue biopsies to view under the microscope. Visual inspection and timing of injuries is thought to be inaccurate. When discussing bruises in a report format, it is important to give two-dimensional measurements and descriptive adjectives for the colors seen.

Laceration

A laceration is a tear in the skin caused by a force being applied to the surface. The force exceeds the elasticity of the skin and causes it to tear, creating jagged edges, abraded or contused margins and small pieces of connective tissue extending between the edges. Lacerations are caused by blunt force trauma where the skin comes in contact with an object or an object strikes the skin. These are commonly seen in motor vehicle accidents, falls, or inflicted trauma such as with a pipe, baseball bat, chair leg, etc. When documenting a laceration, it is necessary to measure the length, width and depth of the injury. Accurate close-up photographs with and without a scale are important also.

Incision

An incision is a cut in the skin, characterized by smooth wound edges without bridging tissue, abraded or contused margins. They are created by sharp-force objects such as knives, scalpels, and sometimes glass. A stab wound is a type of incision, which extends deeper into the body than it measures in length. In contrast, an incised wound is longer than it is deep, and has a slashing quality to it. When documenting incisions, it is necessary to measure their length, width and depth and obtain close-up photographs to evaluate the wound qualities.

Fracture

Fractures are broken bones and are described as open fractures (bone communicates with the skin) or closed fractures (bone fragments are covered by skin). Linear fractures are simple straight lines and can be in the long bones of the extremities or in the skull. Compound fractures are when the bone is shattered into multiple pieces. Depressed fractures describe a piece of the bone being displaced inward into the underlying tissue. It is usually used to describe a skull fracture with displacement of the bone into the brain. Fracture terminology is used when the underlying force is caused by blunt force trauma.

Patterned Injuries

Any of these injuries can have patterned qualities to them and can give the examiner clues as to the type of instrument that may have created the injury. Some common examples of objects that typically leave patterned areas are ropes, belts, electrical cords, pipes, hammers, nightsticks, muzzles of guns, shoes, tires, bumpers/grills of motor vehicles, manual strangulation, bite marks etc. Cylindrical objects (pipes, nightsticks) usually cause a tram like parallel contusion with the distance between the parallel tracks corresponding to the object. Belts cause imprints of the stitching and parallel margins corresponding to the width of the belt. Sometimes the belt is held in a loop and the narrow edge is the one visible or an abrasion of the belt buckle may be seen. Spiral rope patterns are commonly seen as abrasions on the skin in hangings. Hammers have two edges and there are multiple kinds of hammers (carpet, ball, carpenter etc). A regular carpenter hammer tends to cause a curved laceration and if the injury is on the head creates circular depressed skull fractures the diameter of the hammerhead. The claw edge causes two linear lacerations occurring in pairs and corresponding to the length of each of the claws.

Photographic Documentation of Injuries

Identifying which object caused the injury is important in the documentation for judicial purposes. When photographing a patterned injury (or any injury for that matter), it is important to take a systematic approach to it. Overall, a photo of an area to gain perspective where the injury is located is important. Every photo should include case numbers for correct documentation. Some departments do this by including a photo of the call out card (case number, location, name of person being photographed, date etc) at the beginning of the series of photos. Others include a case number in each photo.

The next photo of an injury should be closer but include a reference point (an ear or hand, eye) to determine its right and left position and front or back. It should be close enough to see an outline of the injury.

The next photo should be a close up of the injury and needs to fill the viewfinder. This way the fine characteristics of the wound can later be reviewed. Each close up should include photos with and without measuring scale. It is also advisable to include a color chart on injuries. Color charts are scales of the color spectrum and the grey scale. These are used during processing of the photos to ensure that the color of the processing renders the photo a true rendition of the color seen at the time of the photo. It is a correcting mechanism for the different shades of color and prevents the photo from being too red or blue, too black or white.

Sometimes there are a very large number of injuries to document. At that point, it may be best to do overalls, regional photos for documentation of areas then close-ups of smaller groups or particularly good representations of patterned areas. If a suspect weapon is available, it is best to photo the patterned wound with the suspect weapon adjacent to it. To prevent contamination of the weapon, it may be necessary to bring a close rendition of the object to use as an example or to encase the weapon in a see through wrapping to compare it next to the wound.

When photographing bodies at autopsy, overall photographs are obtained when the body bag is opened, with and without clothing and repeated after washing the body. Evidence procured during the autopsy is photographed as it is obtained (bullets, ligatures, clothing). Overall, photographs include upper, lower halves of the sides of the body, upper, and lower halves of the front and back of body. Close-ups of injuries (bullet wounds, stabs, ligature areas) will be needed as well as pertinent negatives (backs of the hands and arms, sides of the face, back of the head etc) depending on what type of case it is.

When photographing injuries it is important to maintain the proper perspective of the camera to the wound to prevent photographic distortion of the dimensions or shape of the wound. To prevent this, it is important to photograph the wound at a 90-degree angle to the camera. A bite mark ruler is a good one to use in photographs as it includes not only a scale in centimeters, but also a gray scale and three circles. The circles can be viewed in the photos to assure that the photo was taken on the perpendicular; if not the circles will appear oval. Obviously, some injuries can be large and extend over curved areas of the body. To accurately photograph these types of injuries may require more than one photo and to systematically rotate the ruler over the curved surface near the injury and re-photo it.

Chapter 9

...ogy, forensic entomology, ...lectible evidence. Each of ...n be used in forensics and

Laceration
Source - Personal Collection:
Ann Bucholtz

...cision Wound
Source - Personal Collection: Ann Bucholtz

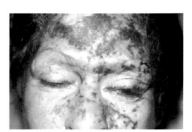

Postmortem Roach Bites
Source Personal Collection: Ann Bucholtz

Patterned Injury (Belt)
Source - Personal Collection:
Ann Bucholtz

Entomologist collecting insects at a
crime scene
Source - www.fbi.gov/hq/lab/ert/slert.htm

SUMMARY

This chapter discussed forensic toxico
forensic botany, and documentation of uncol
the topics included definitions, how the data ca
collection methods.

DISCUSSION QUESTIONS

Vocabulary

- forensic toxicology
- forensic entomology
- forensic botany
- instar
- gas chromatogram
- GC-MS
- urine drug screen
- meconium
- gray scale
- patterned injuries
- abrasion
- contusion
- laceration
- incision
- fracture

ADDITIONAL READING

History of Forensic Science
    http://www.crimelibrary.com/criminal_mind/forensics/toxicology/2.html?sect=6

ENDNOTES

1. www.missouri.edu/~agwww/entomology/chapter1.html
    #history

Chapter 10

Autopsy - The Body As Evidence

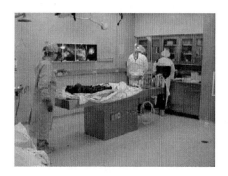

OVERVIEW

In this chapter, the autopsy and body as evidence will be discussed. The difference between a medical examiner and coroner will be clarified. The laws that pertain to reporting death and procedures used during the autopsy will be covered.

CHAPTER OBJECTIVES

After studying this chapter, the student will be able to:

1. Understand the differences between a medical examiner and a coroner system.
2. Understand the types of deaths reportable to the medical examiner or coroner.
3. Understand the purpose of a death certificate
4. Gain an understanding of the different stages of an autopsy and how they are performed.
5. Understand the methods used to obtain toxicology from a body.
6. Understand the principles used in photography of a decedent and their injuries.
7. Gain an understanding of the principles used to estimate the time of death.
8. Understand the changes that occur with an embalming procedure and how it influences establishing the cause of death.
9. Understand how the diagnosis of SIDS is made.
10. Gain an understanding of the organ donation procedure.

HISTORICAL PERSPECTIVES

The beginnings of the investigation of crime through examination of the bodies began in the mid-1100s AD in England with the establishment of the idea of a coroner. When the New World was settled, the English concept came to America and remained until 1915 when the first medical examiner office was established in New York City. Physicians were not formally a part of the coroner system until the late 1800s. In the intervening years there were multiple writings on the subject but perhaps one of the first books is a Chinese one from the mid-1200s AD called "Washing Away of Wrongs" where instruments were compared to injuries and the knowledge was used to identify the suspects.

Forensic pathology is the science of studying a body for disease and trauma for the purpose of establishing the cause and manner of death. This usually involved studying sudden, violent or unexplained deaths and the collection of evidence for expert testimony in court. Expert testimony forms only about one-third of the job description with the majority of time spent performing autopsies. Autopsies are performed to accurately diagnose the extent of trauma, the disease processes and in turn prevent spread of disease and protect public health interests. The dead do speak.

MEDICAL EXAMINER vs. CORONER

The major distinction between the medical examiner system and a coroner system is the qualifications necessary. A coroner is an elected official and usually the only qualification is that they be a registered voter. The position does not require a medical or legal background. Many have served as a public health official, sheriff, funeral director and occasionally, it may be a medical professional. A medical examiner is a physician, either an MD or a DO, with training in pathology and forensic pathology who is appointed to the position by state or local agencies. Individual states may or may not require Board Certification (a national exam by the American Board of Pathologists to ensure basic competence). Forensic pathologists are physicians with specialty training in determining cause of death by autopsy and/or trauma pathology, and can give expert testimony in court. A forensic pathologist may be contracted by a coroner to perform the autopsies for the jurisdiction, but the coroner usually certifies the cause of death on the death certificate. Each state has its own laws as to whether they operate under medical examiner or coroner jurisdiction. Some states are both. The CDC maintains a list of all the medical examiner and coroner jurisdictions in the country.

[To view a current CDC Medical Examiner and Coroner jurisdiction map, visit: www.cdc.gov and search for "MECISPmap1", then click on PowerPoint Presentation.]

MEDICAL EXAMINER LAWS

In general, when a dead body is discovered, law enforcement or the medical examiner's office should be notified. This is especially true if someone has died at home or is outside of a medical facility. This prevents traumatic deaths from escaping investigation.

Death is certified by a clinical physician, medical examiner or coroner. There may be laws forbidding emergency room physicians from certifying the death as it is felt that they may not have complete medical history to do so. In general, a physician who has been attending to the patient may sign the death certificate if he/she feels they are able to base the death on the patient's medical history, and if there is no evidence of an unnatural or traumatic death. In the latter scenario, the attending physician may decline and forward the case to be reviewed by law enforcement and the medical examiner/coroner departments. To prevent the case from escaping their notification, it is wise for the attending doctor to notify the authorities himself or have a dependable representative to do so.

In the case of unnatural deaths, each state has their own specific statutes as to what constitutes a reportable death. Reportable usually is described as anyone with the knowledge of types of deaths that fall under the medical examiner or coroner jurisdiction. In that scenario, hospital permission for autopsy and attending physician certification of the death certificate is invalid procedure. The individual state laws regarding death were based on guidelines provided by the Model Post-Mortem Examinations Act of 1954. The statutes of each state are based on the following:

The Office of Post-Mortem Examinations shall investigate all human deaths of the types listed herewith:

(a) Violent deaths, whether apparently homicidal, suicidal, or accidental, including but not limited to deaths due to thermal, chemical, electrical or radiation injury, and deaths due to criminal abortion, whether apparently self-induced or not;

(b) Sudden deaths not caused by readily recognizable disease;

(c) Deaths under suspicious circumstances;

(d) Deaths of persons, whose bodies are to be cremated, dissected, buried at sea, or otherwise disposed of to be thereafter unavailable for examination;

(e) Deaths of inmates of public institutions not hospitalized therein for organic disease;

(f) Deaths related to disease resulting from employment or to accident while employed;

(g) Deaths related to disease, which might constitute a threat to public health.

WHAT IS A DEATH CERTIFICATE?

A death certificate serves a number of functions. In conjunction with a birth certificate, it serves as a record of someone's existence and death. A death certificate is an official document filed with the local and state vital records departments. It is necessary for families to close bank accounts, claim life insurance and to close out property and estates. It also serves as a means to track vital statistics and compile information concerning frequency and locations of certain reportable deaths for epidemiologic purposes. Certain causes of death must also be reported to the state health board for further epidemiological investigation. These include infectious disease such as newly diagnosed AIDS, sexually transmitted diseases (gonorrhea/syphilis), rabies, plague, polio, anthrax, tuberculosis etc. The public health department can then contact individuals who may have been exposed and implement treatment. The list of reportable diseases varies somewhat from state to state (contact your local health department for the list of reportable diseases). The crime scene investigator's exposures to these health risks at a scene are important. The rationale for wearing gloves and facemasks is not only to prevent contamination of the scene by your DNA but also to prevent your procurement of a potential disease present there.

With the coming of the computer age, electronic death certificates have become available in some states. They have been based on the U.S. Death Certificate prototype.

WHAT IS AN AUTOPSY?

An autopsy is a medical procedure performed by a pathologist to determine the state of disease of the internal organs and in turn to determine why someone has died. The procedure is a multi-step process. The initial portion includes reviewing the circumstances of death and any available medical records. The body is given to the pathologist in a body bag in the state it was at the time of death, preferably with all medical appliances and the clothing left in place as it was at the pronouncement time. The body is usually photographed upon opening the body bag to document the general appearance. External trace evidence on the clothing or surface of the body is collected. Gunshot residue from the hands is obtained prior to manipulation or washing of the body to prevent contamination from materials on the clothing. The hands are examined for adherent trace evidence. Clothing and medical appliances are then removed. The clothing is laid out on clean white sheets to photograph, documenting gunshot or stab areas for later review.

The body is weighed and height is measured. After undressing the body, it is again examined for trace evidence such as fibers, paint chips, semen or hair fibers. At this point a sexual assault kit may be utilized. Injuries, especially gunshot wounds, need to be photographed prior to washing the body as washing can wash away gunshot residue. The body is then washed and re-photographed. Photography involves overall photos: upper half and lower halves both sides, top half and lower half viewed above and from the back. Close-up views taken at 90 degrees from the injury need to be obtained of all the wounds. If there are many wounds, it is helpful to group them including a useful landmark to localize it later in the photograph (such as an ear, jaw, tattoo, umbilicus or hand). Multiple stab and gunshot wounds may be numbered so that they can be individually recognized later and connected to the pathologist's report.

The internal portion of the examination involves making a Y shaped incision over the front of the torso and entering the chest and abdominal cavities. Evidence of internal bleeding is documented by measuring any blood or fluids that may have accumulated in the chest or abdominal cavities. Each of the organs is individually removed, weighed, dissected and biopsied for later microscopic examination. The pathologist examines each of the organs for diseases, abnormalities and trauma that could have resulted in death. The head is examined by making a semicircular incision over the top of the head and a circular skull incision to view the brain.

During this portion of the internal exam, internal evidence will be obtained by the pathologist. This includes toxicology specimens, bullets and paths of the wounds caused by the bullet or knife wounds. Recovery of the bullets will require photography of the recovered fragments with a ruler and case number prior to placing them into a container. Again, the 90-degree rule applies and to ensure this in the photo, a bite mark ruler is a useful type of scale. The circles on the ruler will ensure that the photo was taken properly.

When photographing injuries, it is important to photograph them dirty and clean. If it is a live victim, it isn't helpful to photograph an injury with a dressing covering the wound. It may be necessary to ask for assistance from the medical personnel to obtain the proper perspective in this regard. Be sure to get close-up photos of the wound so the margins can be assessed. The forensic pathologist relies on the edges of a wound to determine entrance and exit gunshot wounds, to determine which blunt object may have caused the injury, or which knife caused the wound.

During the examination, the pathologist generally dictates their findings and records them for later transcription to a written report. Following the autopsy, it can be anywhere from a number of days to weeks to obtain toxicology reports. The pathologist will also examine the biopsies of the organs taken during the internal examination under the microscope to document diagnoses and sometimes date injuries.

TIME OF DEATH

At best, time of death can only be estimated in a broad range and is made by the medical examiner or coroner. It can only be made prior to the body being moved and as soon after the body is discovered as possible. To estimate the time elapsed since death, the following are evaluated:

Rigor Mortis

Rigor is the postmortem stiffening of the body. It is caused by chemical changes that occur in the muscles following death. Every muscle will undergo the change but it is more apparent in small muscles sooner (jaw, hands, infants, elderly) than in larger muscles (thigh, upper arms, body builder). The saying 'stiff as a board' after death is true. Initially, the body is like a plank. The stiffening begins immediately after death, but usually isn't generalized until 4 to 6 hours. It will remain that way for about 10 to 12 hours, at which time the stiffening begins to pass. At this point the rigor is easily broken (the joints will bend easily when flexed) and eventually will pass totally until the body becomes limp. This may take more than 24 hours. The above time frames are based on average climate conditions. Hotter temperatures shorten the time frames; cooler ones lengthen it.

Rigor must be assessed prior to moving the body as the movement will 'break' the rigor and the time 'resets' from that point. Rigor sets in the position of gravity. If someone dies lying in bed, the rigor will show the position of the person's hands at the time of death. Rigor is useful to determine if the body was moved prior to the site it was found. An example is someone killed in their easy chair in the morning and left sitting until evening when the body was moved and dumped by the side of the road. The rigor will have established in the sitting position. If unbroken during the move, the body will still be sitting when dumped, a position contrary to gravity. If the person were killed and dumped prior to rigor, the body will assume a position corresponding to gravitational forces.

Livor Mortis

Livor is the pink color of the skin associated with the postmortem settling of blood. It occurs when the heart ceases to beat and the blood no longer circulates. Blood settles in the vessels closest to the gravitational pull. Livor begins immediately upon death but may not be apparent until 4 to 6 hours after death. In the early period of 4 to 6 hours it 'blanches' or when pressed upon, it diffuses the blood and appears white (instead of pink). It remains blanchable until 8 to 12 hours, when it becomes 'fixed'. This means that pressure on the skin no longer diffuses the blood and it remains red with pressure. These blanching and fixed qualities are helpful in estimating the time of death.

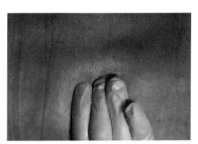

Image 10.1: Livor with pressure is blanchable in the early postmortem period
Source - Personal collection: Ann Bucholtz

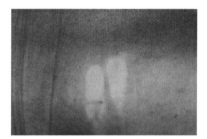

Image 10.2: Blanchable Livor
Source - Personal collection: Ann Bucholtz

Livor is also useful to determine if the body was moved after death. While livor is blanchable, it signifies that the blood is still fluid and moves if the body is moved. An example is if someone dies on his or her back. The pink livor will be evident on their back. If the body is moved in the early postmortem period then placed face down, the livor will move from the back to the front. The person will have the pink discoloration over their back and their front, which is not possible unless they were moved.

The rate which livor appears, blanches and becomes fixed is also dependent on environmental conditions. The warmer the environmental temperature, the more rapid the transition. The cooler the conditions, livor onset is slower and it appears a brighter pink. Bright pink livor is also associated with carbon monoxide or cyanide poisoning.

Algor Mortis

Following death the body's temperature approaches the ambient temperature of the environment. Investigators assess the body temperature by inserting a thermometer into the liver tissue or rectum to obtain a core temperature. Calculation of the time of death from the rate the temperature has fallen assumes that the person had a normal body temperature at death (which may not be true if they were febrile) and that the environmental temperature is less than the body temperature (which may not be true if body is found in a hot environment, such as the dessert where the the body temperature will rise). Body temperature may be useful in a person who presents with a fever or the death is witnessed.

Gastric Contents

Gastric emptying usually takes 4 to 6 hours after a meal. Again, this is a rough estimate and depends on the amount and type of food eaten. Confrontations, which cause adrenalin release, will slow gastric emptying. An example where it might be useful is identifying the food material eaten and comparing it to the last known meal. It is not very useful in determining the time of death in most cases.

PROCEDURES IN AN AUTOPSY

Collection of Toxicology

Routine Toxicology

Routine toxicology includes the following fluids or tissues, if they are present: vitreous, whole blood, urine, gastric contents, bile, liver tissue and brain tissue.

Vitreous fluid is the thick clear fluid present inside the eye. It is aspirated with a syringe or a vacuum assisted tube. It is useful to determine electrolytes, glucose and renal function.

Blood is generally collected with a syringe. The best specimen is from the femoral vein (externally) or the iliac veins (internally) and is known as peripheral blood. These locations are beneficial because they reflect the drug levels seen by the body and are not artificially elevated because of the absorption from the lungs or gut. Some drugs are stored in the heart muscle and upon death and cell breakdown, the drugs can be released from the cells into the blood. This would cause artificially elevated levels. To avoid these complications in later interpretation of drug values, it is best to obtain the best sample possible, which is peripheral blood.

Sometimes this is not possible, especially in children, decomposed bodies, or those who have died of excessive blood loss (known as exsanguination and seen in motor vehicle accidents, gunshot wounds or stab wounds). In this case, some blood is better than no blood and cardiac samples or even cavity (potential spaces in the body such as the pleural cavity, pericardial sac or even the abdominal cavity) blood may be obtained. Cavity blood is not as desirable because of the potential contamination of the blood by a ruptured stomach or bowel. If the decedent recently ingested a drug or alcohol and the stomach or bowel contents leaked into blood that had accumulated in the cavity (hemothorax is blood in the chest cavity; hemoperitoneum is blood in the abdomen) the blood-alcohol or drug value obtained from this blood will be falsely elevated because of the high concentration of the substance in the ingested material.

Not all bodies received in a medical examiner or coroner's office are autopsied. It is necessary to acquire toxicology on closed bodies. Femoral blood from the groin is the first choice; other choices (in order of preference) include subclavian, then cardiac blood. These latter two sites are prone to contamination from a pleural or even abdominal cavity and the results need to be interpreted with caution for the reason outlined above.

Urine is an extremely useful fluid for toxicology analysis because of the ease of its use in screening analysis. It is aspirated with a syringe or vacuum tube device much like vitreous fluid. It can be obtained in closed bodies by inserting a syringe through the skin near the pubic region. In autopsied bodies, the bladder is exposed and the urine is aspirated with a syringe.

Bile is a thick green fluid, which is contained in the gallbladder on the underside of the liver and is obtained with a syringe or vacuum tube device. Because it is a liquid and reflects breakdown products of drugs metabolized by the liver, it is easier to use than emulsified liver tissue. It can usually only be obtained from an open body.

Gastric contents are the emulsified, partially digested remains of food within the stomach and are usually poured into a cuplike container. They are examined for the type of contents including pill residue or food fragments.

Liver and brain tissue are usually collected as small pieces (30 grams or so) into a cup container and are stored frozen. The tissue is emulsified prior to being analyzed by the laboratory.

Special Toxicology (inhalants, cultures, genetic screening)

Some cases require special toxicology or special preservation of the blood. Many drugs continue to breakdown and convert from their parent drug to metabolites after the person has died. This breakdown can be prevented by the use of certain preservatives. Most times, it is through the use of a material called sodium fluoride. DNA or blood typing preservation requires a different preservative called EDTA. Some testing cannot be performed on blood with any preservative such as for HIV or Hepatitis testing.

Blood cultures are a type of collection of the blood fluids for evaluation of bacterial growth to determine if the cause of death was by an infectious disease. To prevent contamination by postmortem bacteria or those present in the air of the morgue, these specimens are usually the first ones obtained after the body is opened. The specimens are drawn with a sterile syringe and placed in special culture media obtained from the laboratory.

Spinal fluid cultures are performed where infection has an undiagnosed role in the death. This fluid is obtained from the back of the head at the base of the skull or from the lower back utilizing a syringe that has been inserted into the spine to withdraw the fluid.

Lung cultures are also a part of the culture triad. In this instance, a small piece of lung is removed with a sterile scalpel and placed into a sterile cup or tube. All cultures are generally sent to a specialty microbiology laboratory for incubation and identification of suspect microorganisms.

Genetic screens are generally performed on children, infants and fetuses that die of no visible means such as trauma. Some genetic diseases are not screened for at birth and may take time to manifest themselves. In some children, the initial symptom may be death. To prevent further deaths in the family, screening is done to diagnose and discover these causes. The screening is done on small blood droplets preserved on special filter paper provided by the specialty screening company.

Inhalants are difficult to detect in toxicology screens because of their volatility and gas properties. They easily dissipate after death and especially if cardiopulmonary resuscitation has been performed. Aspiration of tracheal air or placing lung tissue in a closed container for headspace analysis may be the only way to make the diagnosis. Even then, the results may be negative and the diagnosis would be made based on scene investigation (finding huffing paraphernalia) or residue on the skin or clothing (gold paint or whiteout droplets on the hands or face).

FAA Kit for Aircraft crashes

The FAA provides a special toxicology kit requesting tissues and fluids for toxicological and alcohol analysis of the flight crew. In general, the kit includes the necessary containers and requests the following materials:

- Vitreous
- Blood
- Bile
- Urine
- Gastric contents
- Spinal fluid
- Brain tissue
- Heart tissue
- Lung
- Muscle
- Liver
- Spleen
- Kidney

In general, the medical examiner or coroner would perform their own toxicology testing in conjunction with the submission of these tissues to the FAA for evaluation.

Collection of DNA

Collection of DNA samples in fresh bodies is relatively easy and needs to be performed on all decedents being evaluated by a medical examiner or coroner's office. At the time of death only a limited amount of information as to one's identity is available. Issues related to identity or paternity issues may later arise and the DNA sample may be the only way to resolve these questions. A 1 to 2 inch spot of air-dried blood on filter paper and properly labeled, placed in an envelope and frozen is adequate (Image 10.3). It should be obtained at the same time as the remainder of the toxicology sampling.

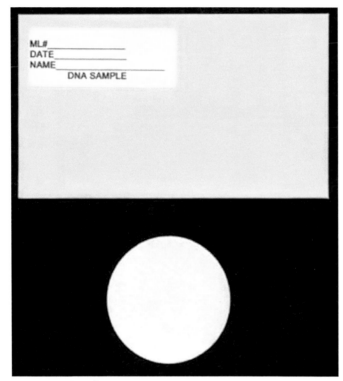

Image 10.3: DNA filter paper and storage envelope.
(Source - Personal collection: Ann Bucholtz)

Collection of DNA samples on decomposed bodies is much more challenging. In some cases the bloody fluid in the body may provide the needed specimen and it should be preserved on a filter paper, dried and placed in an envelope. Sometimes, the bloody fluid expressed from the spleen may be preserved in this fashion. The biggest problem in decomposed bodies is the specimens are overwhelmed by postmortem bacterial overgrowth, which is a natural part of the decomposition process. In these cases, the best specimen is a fragment of deep muscle (thigh), a portion of bone (femur) and in badly decomposed (skeletal) or charred remains teeth are possible sources of DNA.

Microscopic Examination

Each autopsied body usually has biopsies taken of each of the

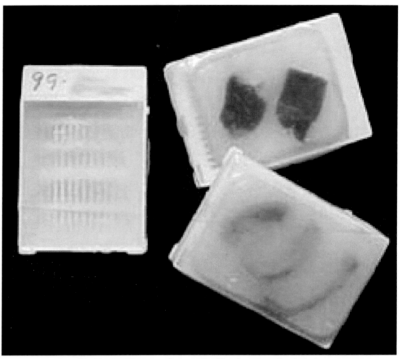

Image 10.4 Paraffin blocks (Source - Personal collection: Ann Bucholtz)

organs. These are placed in small plastic cases and processed through a machine, which preserves the tissue and encases it within paraffin (Image 10.4). The paraffin serves as a medium to harden the tissue so that it may be sliced in micron thick sections and placed on a glass slide Image 10.5). The slide then is stained different colors to highlight the

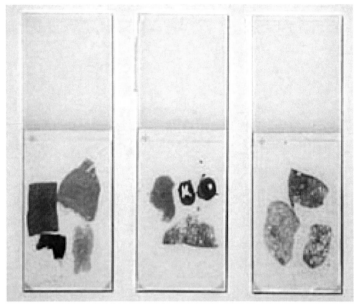

Image 10.5 Microscopic slides are examined by the pathologist under the microscope to detect the presence of disease (Source - Personal collection: Ann Bucholtz)

differences in the nuclei and cytoplasm of the cells. The pathologist can then review the slides and make diagnoses regarding disease processes called microscopic diagnoses. The importance of this is the fact that the blocks are retained for at least 10 years by the hospital or medical examiners offices. This tissue can serve as a valuable source of DNA for comparison to evidence or skeletal remains.

EMBALMING

Embalming is the process of preserving the body after death. The process involves removing the blood and body fluids and replacing them with a formaldehyde solution to delay the decomposition process. Removal of the blood involves incising the skin at the base of the neck, incising the jugular vein and inserting a needle into the carotid artery. The needle is attached to a pump containing the formalin solution, which is forced under pressure throughout the body. The formalin flows through the arterial system and the blood drains through the open jugular vein. The trunk does not generally perfuse well with the formalin and to aid the preservation, a large trochar or aspirating needle-like device is inserted into the abdomen to aspirate gastric and bowel contents. Formalin is then infused into the cavity. Because of the large number of artifacts produced by the trochar work and the removal of the fluids, accurate diagnoses of death can be very difficult to impossible. For this reason, medical examiners and coroners prefer to receive bodies prior to embalming and in some states, the law requires it.

STATE LAWS REGARDING DONOR ISSUES

Organ donation is regulated by the Uniform Anatomical Gift Act, which allows individuals to make a choice for organ donation and for families to allow donation.

Each state varies in the actual procedure for organ donation. Organs can be donated from one who is brain dead but on life support. In general, brain death is defined as a brain with no hope of meaningful recovery but the heart and other vital organs continue to function. It is diagnosed by evaluating the brain waves through an EEG. There are also cases where the person has died but has useful tissues (corneas, heart valves, bone tissue or skin) which can be placed into an organ bank and donated to patients at a later time. Organs can be harvested if the dying individual requested their organs be donated (usually on the driver's license) or if a family member grants consent for their donation. The regulating agencies of hospitals have also required that hospital personnel must notify donor procurement agencies of all death and potential deaths so that family members may be approached for potential donation. In some states, traumatic deaths also require the consent of the medical examiner or coroner prior to donation. For optimal tissue viability, the death must be witnessed.

SUDDEN DEATH IN CHILDREN

Sudden Infant Death Syndrome (SIDS), also known as unexplained sudden death syndrome (SUDS), is a condition of infants less than one year of age where the infant suddenly dies. They generally have no symptoms of illness or history of any life threatening condition, an investigation of the scene of death reveals no hazards for possible asphyxia or smothering, and the autopsy discovers no disease or congenital abnormalities. Toxicology screens are negative. Since the diagnosis is made on the absence of findings, a thorough investigation needs to be performed. To aid the investigating officer, the CDC has developed guidelines and a checklist to ensure that all areas of the death have been questioned. In the past, families have been interrogated when their child died. This has lead to some states enacting laws for law enforcement and first responders to be educated regarding SIDS and that not all infant deaths reflect criminal intent. [*See the CDC Guidelines and Checklist for SIDS (Fig. 10.1) on the following pages.*]

Many states continue to use this checklist. An on-line format is coming into favor because of the ease in transmitting data from the investigative agency to the medical examiner/coroner who will require this information to properly evaluate the circumstances of death. This format has the ability to attach digital photographs to the form. It is sponsored by the CDC and will allow a nationwide database for surveillance and prevention (www.cdc.gov/reproductivehealth /sids/index.html).

Figure 10.1 Guidelines for using the CDC SIDS Forms

All sudden and unexplained deaths among infants up to 1 year of age may be investigated by using the SUIDIRF. Local statutes define which infant deaths must be investigated, but these deaths usually include any in which the cause or circum-stances of death are unknown (including deaths that are apparently due to a natural cause but cannot be confirmed by medical records, a personal physician, or a witness to the death) and any for which child abuse or neglect is suspected. The SUIDIRF is not copyrighted and can be used with or without modification by any agency involved in investigating SUIDs. The protocol is intended for use primarily by medical examiners, coroners, death investigators, and police officers. Public health workers should ensure that local medical examiners and coroners are familiar with this report and the SUIDIRF.

Because the SUIDIRF is available in electronic form, it may be modified to meet the needs of individual investigators or agencies. For example, the data items may be rearranged, larger spaces for writing can be created, and data items may be added. To ensure uniform collection of core data items, items currently on the SUIDIRF should not be deleted or ignored. Further, these items may be important to other agencies or organizations examining trends. CDC is investigating options for computerized data entry and report generation in the SUIDIRF format.

The death scene investigation is an essential component of a thorough investigation of SUIDs. Information gathered during the scene investigation augments that obtained from an autopsy and review of the infant's clinical history. Information gathered during a SUID scene investigation can help the pathologist interpret postmortem findings and rule in or rule out accidental, environmental, and unnatural causes of deaths, including child abuse and neglect. Although the ultimate goal of a SUID scene investigation is to accurately assign a cause of death, no less important goals are identifying health threats posed by consumer products, identifying and understanding risk factors associated with SUIDs, and using the opportunity to refer families to grief counseling and support groups. These guidelines set the stage for standardized investigative procedures, data collection instruments, and training for SUID scene investigations, and they underscore the central role of medical examiners and coroners in public health surveillance and epidemiologic research of SUIDs.

SUDDEN UNEXPLAINED INFANT DEATH
INVESTIGATION REPORT FORM (SUIDIRF) 3.96

Case number _____

Infant's full name _____	Age _____	DOB _____
Home address _____	Race _____	Sex _____
City, state, zip _____	Ethnicity _____	
County _____	SS# _____	

Police complaint number _____ Police department _____

I. CIRCUMSTANCES OF DEATH

Action	Date	Time	By whom (person or agency)	Remarks
ME/C notified				Receipt by:
NOK notified				Person:
Scene visit				__ ME/C staff __ Other agency __ Not done
Scene address				
Condition of infant when found			__ Dead (D) __ Unresponsive (U) __ In distress (I) __ NA (N)	
Sequence of events before death:				

Event	Date	Time	Location (street, city, state, county, zip code)	
Injury				
Discovery				
Arrival			Hospital: Transport by:	
Actual death			__ On scene (S) __ Emergency room (E) __ Inpatient (I) __ En route or DOA (D) __ During surgery (O)	
Pronounced dead			By whom: License #: Where:	

Event	Date	Time	By whom (person)	Remarks
Infant placed				Place:
Known alive				Place:
Infant found				Place:
First response				Type:
EMS called				From where:
EMS response			Agency:	
Police response			Agency:	

Place of fatal event	Describe type of place:
__ Witness in room or area (W) or __ Unwitnessed (U) __ At own home (H) or __ Away from home (A) __ Indoors (I) or __ Outdoors (O) __ In vehicle (V) or __ Not in vehicle (N)	

SUDDEN UNEXPLAINED INFANT DEATH
INVESTIGATION REPORT FORM (SUIDIRF) 3.96   Case number _____

II. BASIC MEDICAL INFORMATION

Health care provider
for infant: Phone:

Medical history	___ Not investigated (X) ___ Unk (U) ___ No past problems (N) ___ Medical problems (P)

Medical source	___ Physician (P) ___ Other health care provider (H) ___ Other (O)
	___ Medical records (M) ___ Family (F) ___ None (N)

Specific infant medical history	Yes	No	Unk	Remarks

A. Problems during labor or delivery
   Birth hospital:
   Birth city and state:				

B. Maternal illness or complications during pregnancy Number of prenatal visits:				
C. Major birth defects				

D. Infant was one of multiple births (e.g., a twin)
   Birth weight:
   Gestational age at birth (weeks):				

E. Hospitalization of infant after initial discharge				
F. Emergency room visits in past 2 weeks				
G. Known allergies				
H. Growth and weight gain considered normal				
I. Exposure to contagious disease in past 2 weeks				
J. Illness in past 2 weeks				
K. Lethargy, crankiness, or excessive crying in past 48 hours				
L. Appetite changes in past 48 hours				
M. Vomiting or choking in past 48 hours				
N. Fever or excessive sweating in past 48 hours				
O. Diarrhea or stool changes in past 48 hours				
P. Infant has ever stopped breathing or turned blue				
Q. Infant was ever breast-fed				
R. Vaccinations in past 72 hours				
S. Infant injury or other condition not mentioned above				
T. Deceased siblings				

Diet in past 2 weeks included: ___ Breast milk   ___ Formula   ___ Cow's milk   ___ Solids
   Date and time of last meal:
   Content of last meal:

Medication history	___ Not investigated (X) ___ Unk (U) ___ Rx (P) ___ OTC (O) ___ Home remedies (H) ___ None (N)
Emergency medical treatment	___ None (N) ___ CPR (R) ___ Transfusion (T) ___ IV fluids (F) ___ Surgery (S)

Medicine names and doses; if prescription, include Rx number, Rx date, and name of pharmacy:	Describe nature and duration of resuscitation and treatments used to revive infant:	Describe any known injuries or marks on infant created or observed during resuscitation or treatment:

**SUDDEN UNEXPLAINED INFANT DEATH
INVESTIGATION REPORT FORM (SUIDIRF) 3.96**   Case number _____

III. HOUSEHOLD ENVIRONMENT				
Action	**Yes**	**No**	**Unk**	**Remarks**
A. House was visited				
B. Evidence of alcohol abuse				
C. Evidence of drug abuse				
D. Serious physical or mental illness in household				
E. Police have been called to home in past				
F. Prior contact with social services				
G. Documented history of child abuse				
H. Odors, fumes, or peeling paint in household				
I. Dampness, visible standing water, or mold growth				
J. Pets in household				

Type of dwelling: _____ Water source: _____ Number of bedrooms: _____

Main language in home: _____ Estimated annual income: _____ On public assistance ___ Yes ___ No

Number of adults (≥18 years of age): ___ and children (<18 years of age): ___ living in household. Total = ___ people.

Number of smokers in household: ___ Does usual caregiver smoke? ___ Yes ___ No ___ Unk If yes, ___ cigarettes/day

Maternal information Age: ___ ___ Married (M) ___ Divorced (D) ___ Single (S) ___ Widowed (W) Cohabiting w/partner: ___ Yes ___ No Education (years): ___ ___ Employed (E) ___ Not employed (N)

IV. INFANT AND ENVIRONMENT		

___ In crib (C) ___ In bed (B) ___ Other (O)   ___ Sleeping alone (A) ___ Sleeping with others (O)   ___ NA (N)   Temperature of area: _____

Body position when placed   ___ Unk ___ Back ___ Stomach ___ Side ___ Other

Body position when found   ___ Unk ___ Back ___ Stomach ___ Side ___ Other

Face position when found   ___ Unk ___ To left ___ To right ___ Facedown ___ Face up ___ To side

Nose or mouth was covered or obstructed   ___ Unk ___ No ___ Yes

Postmortem changes when found   ___ Unk ___ None ___ Rigor ___ Lividity ___ Other

Number of cover or blanket layers on infant: ___   ___ Covers on infant (C) ___ Wrapped (W) ___ No covers (N)

Sleeping or supporting surface: _____   Clothing: _____

Other items in contact with infant: _____   Items in crib or immediate environment: _____

Devices operating in room: _____   Cooling source in room: ___ On (+) ___ Central (C) ___ None (N) ___ Off (-) ___ Space (S)   Heat source in room: ___ On (+) ___ Central (C) ___ None (N) ___ Off (-) ___ Space (S)

Item collected	Yes	No	Item collected	Yes	No	Number of scene photos taken: ___
Baby bottle			Apnea monitor			Other items collected:
Formula			Medicines			
Diaper			Pacifier			
Clothing			Bedding			

**SUDDEN UNEXPLAINED INFANT DEATH
INVESTIGATION REPORT FORM (SUIDIRF) 3.96**   **Case number** _____

V. INTERVIEW AND PROCEDURAL TRACKING

Contact	Name	Date	Time	Phone	Relationship to infant
Mother					
Father					
Usual caregiver					
Last caregiver					
Placer					
Last witness					
Finder					
First responder					
EMS caller					
EMS responder					
Police					

Alternate contact person: Phone:

Action	Date	Time	Action			
Medical record review for infant			Doll reenactment performed	___ Yes	___ No	
Medical record review for mother			Scene diagram completed	___ Yes	___ No	
Physician or provider interview			Body diagram completed	___ Yes	___ No	
Referral to social or SIDS services			Detailed protocol completed	___ Yes	___ No	___ NA
Cause of death discussed with family			Other:			

VI. OVERALL PRELIMINARY SUMMARY

Notes to pathologist performing autopsy:

Indications that an environmental hazard, drug, poison, or consumer product contributed to death ___ Yes ___ No	Organ or tissue donation requested by family or agency ___ Yes ___ No ___ Unk

Cause of death: ___ **Presumed SIDS**   ___ **Suspect trauma or injury**   ___ **Other**

VII. CASE DISPOSITION

Case disposition	___ Case declined (D) due to ___ Topic (T) ___ Locale (L)	___ Case accepted (J) for ___ Autopsy (A) ___ Inspection (I) ___ Certification (C)
Body disposition	___ Brought in for exam (E) ___ Brought in for holding or claim (C) ___ Released from site (R)	
Who will sign DC?		
Transport agent:		Funeral home:
Investigator and affiliation:	Date:	
	Number of supplement pages attached:	

**SUDDEN UNEXPLAINED INFANT DEATH
INVESTIGATION REPORT FORM (SUIDIRF) 3.96**   Case number _____

SCENE DIAGRAM

Instructions

1) Use figure at right for a rectangular room, and use figure below right for a square room. Use a supplementary page to draw an unusually shaped room.

2) Indicate the following on the diagram (check when done):
___ North direction
___ Windows and doors
___ Wall lengths
     Ceiling height: _____
___ Location of furniture
___ Location of crib or bed
___ Body location when found
___ Location of other objects in room
___ Location of heating and cooling supplies and returns

3) Make additional notes or drawings in available spaces as needed.

4) Check all that apply about heat source:
___ Gas furnace or boiler
___ Electric furnace or boiler
___ Forced air
___ Steam or hot water
___ Electric baseboard
     Other: _____
___ None

5) Complete the following:
     Thermostat setting: _____
     Thermostat reading: _____
     Actual room temperature: _____
     Outside temperature: _____

SUDDEN UNEXPLAINED INFANT DEATH
INVESTIGATION REPORT FORM (SUIDIRF) 3.96   Case number _____

BABY DIAGRAM

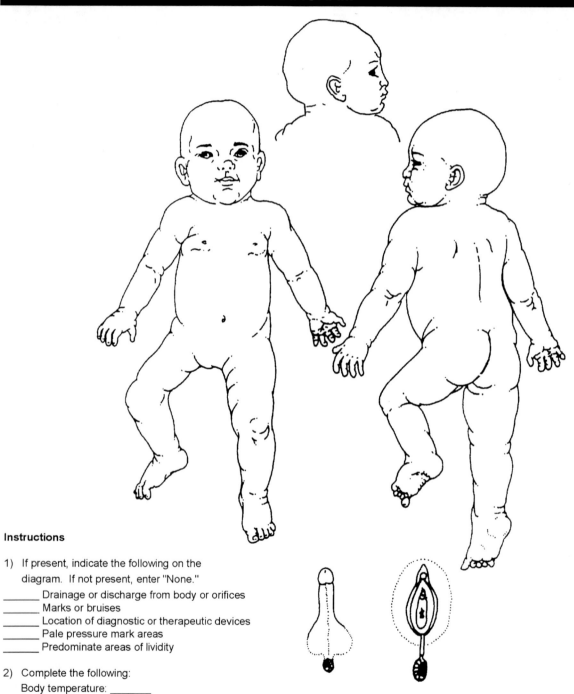

Instructions

1) If present, indicate the following on the
    diagram. If not present, enter "None."
    _____ Drainage or discharge from body or orifices
    _____ Marks or bruises
    _____ Location of diagnostic or therapeutic devices
    _____ Pale pressure mark areas
    _____ Predominate areas of lividity

2) Complete the following:
    Body temperature: _____
    Source of temperature: _____

UDDEN UNEXPLAINED INFANT DEATH
IVESTIGATION REPORT FORM (SUIDIRF) 3.96

Case number _____

SUIDIRF SUPPLEMENT

DISASTER PREPAREDNESS AND MASS FATALITIES

The Aviation Disaster Family Assistance Act of 1996 gives the National Transportation Safety Board (NTSB) the responsibility of investigating accidents occurring in transportation related situations and aiding the families of victims of aircraft accidents occurring in U.S. Immediately upon being notified of an accident, the National Transportation Safety Board contacts the local medical examiner to jointly assess the situation to determine if the Federal government can assist in the recovery and identification of fatalities. The medical examiner may request Federal assistance. The NTSB or the medical examiner can request the Office of Emergency Preparedness, United States Public Health Service (USPHS) to activate the Disaster Mortuary Operational Response Team (DMORT). The DMORT members are composed of private citizens each with a particular field of expertise. Their licensure and certification is recognized by all states and they are compensated for their duty time by the Federal government. They assist the medical examiner with recovery, identification and body preparation of the deceased victims in mass fatality incidents. The team consists of forensic pathologists, odontologists, anthropologists, funeral directors, finger print experts, and other technicians. Many have experience with other aviation disasters, as well as experience involving natural disasters. With the request for DMORT, the emergency mobile mortuary can be mobilized from Rockville, Maryland or Denver, Colorado. It contains a complete morgue with the necessary prepackaged equipment and supplies to support each workstation.

Generally speaking, the local medical examiner or coroner has jurisdiction and determines if autopsies will be conducted. The NTSB has specific requirements that the flight crew is autopsied and full toxicology tests are performed. Depending on the circumstances of the crash, the NTSB investigator-in-charge will consult with the medical examiner or coroner to determine if additional autopsies are required. Dental records and x-rays along with fingerprints are normally the primary methods used in victim identification. DNA will be used as a last resort and only after all conventional means of identification are exhausted.

SUMMARY

In this chapter, the role of the medical examiner and the autopsy as evidence were reviewed. Methods to collect toxicology, FAA materials and DNA were discussed. Photography skills needed at the autopsy were reviewed. Other topics of current interest include SIDS and disaster preparedness.

DISCUSSION TOPICS

Vocabulary

- coroner
- medical examiner
- embalming
- epidemiology
- FAA kit
- vitreous
- SIDS
- rigor mortis
- livor mortis
- algor mortis
- DMORT
- NTSB

REVIEW QUESTIONS

1. Compare and contrast the difference between a coroner and a medical examiner system. Identify the system present in your state.

2. List the general types of cases, which are reportable to the medical examiner or coroner. Identify your state laws pertaining to reportable deaths.

3. Discuss the artifacts created by embalming and how they affect establishing the cause of death.

4. Outline the 3 main factors utilized in establishing an estimate for time of death.

5. List the pertinent negatives necessary to make the diagnosis of SIDS.

6. Identify what DMORT is and the role it plays in a medical examiner system.

7. Discuss how paraffin blocks might prove to be a useful investigative tool.

8. Discuss the procedures used to photograph a body during an autopsy.

9. List the major steps of an autopsy.

10. Discuss 3 different DNA collection techniques and when each might be used.

ADDITIONAL READING

Model Postmortem Examinations Act
    www.cdc.gov/epo/dphsi/mecisp/post-mortem.htm

Guidelines for Prevention of Transmission of Human
    Immunodeficiency Virus and Hepatitis B Virus to Health-Care and Public-Safety Workers
     www.cdc.gov/mmwr/preview/mmwrhtml/00001450.htm
    www.cdc.gov/mmwr/preview/mmwrhtml/rr5308a1.htm

Medical Examiners, Coroners and Biologic Terrorism, A Guidebook for Surveillance and Case Management
    www.cdc.gov/mmwr/PDF/rr/rr4510.pdf

CDC Sudden Unexplained Infant Death Initiative
    www.cdc.gov/reproductivehealth/SIDS/index.html

Chapter 11

Death Certification

OVERVIEW

In this chapter, the death certificate, cause and manner of death will be discussed. What a forensic anthropologist and odontologist are, the procedures used to identify and fingerprint a body in addition to the special problems associated with skeletal remains will be covered.

CHAPTER OBJECTIVES

After studying this chapter, the student will be able to:
1. Understand the importance of the death certificate both as a vital record document and to the family.
2. Understand the difference between cause and manner of death.
3. Gain an understanding of the methods used to fingerprint a decedent.
4. Gain an understanding of the information that a forensic anthropologist may provide.
5. Understand what skeletal remains are and the basic procedures used to identify them.
6. Understand what procedures are performed prior to release of unidentified remains to burial.
7. Understand what data can be provided by a forensic dentist.
8. Understand what problems are associated with identifying an unknown decedent through the NCIC system.

HISTORICAL PERSPECTIVES

Most states adopted the use of death certificates in the early 1900s. Prior to that some of the large cities kept death records or some of the early American states had records but they were not required.[1] Death certificates have evolved into a necessary component of the death process.

Forensic anthropology is a branch of forensic science involving the study of skeletal trauma, recovery of skeletal remains and in turn formulating opinions concerning the age, race, sex, stature and circumstances of death. Most forensic anthropologists are graduates with undergraduate degrees in anthropology and seek masters or PhD degrees in forensic anthropology programs. Forensic anthropology became recognized with the publication of "The Human Skeleton" by Dr. Krogman in the mid-1900s.

WHAT IS A DEATH CERTIFICATE?

A death certificate serves a number of functions. In conjunction with a birth certificate, it serves as a record of someone's existence and death. A death certificate is an official document filed with the local county and in turn, state vital records departments.

Eventually, it is reported nationally to the Centers for Disease Control (CDC) where statistics are calculated regarding the incidences of reported diseases and injuries. Because of heightened awareness of identity theft, the new initiative is to link birth certificates to death certificates to prevent formation of new identities. Often identity thieves obtain new identities by searching newspaper obituaries and use them to request birth certificates. These are then used to obtain all the necessary remaining documents to create the new identity. By linking the death and birth certificates, this avenue of identity theft can be curtailed.

The Vital Statistics Registration System in the United States

Responsible Person or Agency	*Birth Certificate*	*Death Certificate*	*Fetal Death Report*
Hospital authority	1. Completes entire certificate using mother and facility worksheets. 2. Files certificate with local office or State office per State law.	When death occurs in hospital, may initiate preparation of certificate: Completes information on name, date, and place of death; obtains certification of cause of death from physician; and gives certificate to funeral director. NOTE: If the attending physician is unavailable to certify to the cause of death, some States allow a hospital physician to certify to only the fact and time of death. With legal pronouncement of the death and permission of the attending physician, the body can then be released to the funeral director. The attending physician still must complete the cause-of-death section prior to final disposition of the body.	1. Completes entire report using patient and facility worksheets. 2. Obtains cause of fetal death from physician. 3. Obtains authorization for final disposition of fetus. 4. Files report with local office or State office per State law.
Funeral director	⇓	1. Obtains personal facts about decedent and completes certificate. 2. Obtains certification of cause of death from attending physician or medical examiner or coroner. 3. Obtains authorization for final disposition per State law. 4. Files certificate with local office or State office per State law.	If fetus is to be buried, the funeral director is responsible for obtaining authorization for final disposition. NOTE: In some States, the funeral director, or person acting as such, is responsible for all duties shown under hospital authority.
Physician or other professional attendant	For inhospital birth, verifies accuracy of medical information and signs certificate. For out-of-hospital birth, duties are same as those for hospital authority, shown above.	Completes certification of cause of death and signs certificate.	Provides cause of fetal death and information not available from the medical records.
Local office* (may be local registrar or city or county health department)	1. Verifies completeness and accuracy of certificate and queries incomplete or inconsistent certificates. 2. If authorized by State law, makes copy or index for local use. 3. Sends certificates to State registrar.	1. Verifies completeness and accuracy of certificate and queries incomplete or inconsistent certificates. 2. If authorized by State law, makes copy or index for local use. 3. If authorized by State law, issues authorization for final disposition on receipt of completed certificate. 4. Sends certificates to State registrar.	If State law requires routing of fetal death reports through local office, performs the same functions as shown for the birth and death certificate.
City and county health departments	1. Use data derived from these records in allocating medical and nursing services. 2. Follow up on infectious diseases. 3. Plan programs. 4. Measure effectiveness of services. 5. Conduct research studies.		
State registrar, office of vital statistics	1. Queries incomplete or inconsistent information. 2. Maintains files for permanent reference and is the source of certified copies. 3. Develops vital statistics for use in planning, evaluating, and administering State and local health activities and for research studies. 4. Compiles health-related statistics for State and civil divisions of State for use of the health department and other agencies and groups interested in the fields of medical science, public health, demography, and social welfare. 5. Sends data for all events filed to the National Center for Health Statistics.		
Centers for Disease Control and Prevention, National Center for Health Statistics	1. Evaluates quality of State vital statistics data and works with States to assure quality. 2. Compiles national statistical data file and runs edits to fully process data. 3. Prepares and publishes national statistics of births, deaths, and fetal deaths; constructs the official U.S. life tables and related actuarial tables. 4. Conducts health and social research studies based on vital records and on sampling surveys linked to records. 5. Conducts research and methodological studies in vital statistics methods, including the technical, administrative, and legal aspects of vital records registration and administration. 6. Maintains a continuing technical assistance program to improve the quality and usefulness of vital statistics. 7. Provides leadership and coordination in the development of standard certificates and report and model laws.		

* Some States do not have local vital registration offices. In these States, the certificates or reports are transmitted directly to the State office of vital statistics.

Figure 11.1 The Vital Statistics Registration System in the United States

A death certificate is necessary for families to close bank accounts, claim life insurance and to close out property and estates. It also serves as a means to track vital statistics and compile information concerning frequency and locations of certain reportable deaths for epidemiologic purposes, locally, statewide and within the United States. Certain causes of death must also be reported to the state health board for further investigation. These include infectious disease such as newly diagnosed AIDS, sexually transmitted diseases (gonorrhea/syphilis), rabies, plague, polio, anthrax, tuberculosis etc. The public health department can then contact individuals who may have been exposed and implement treatment. The list of reportable diseases varies somewhat from state to state (contact your local health department for the list of reportable diseases). The crime scene investigator's exposures to these health risks are also important. The rationale for wearing gloves and facemasks is not only to prevent contamination of the scene by your DNA but also to prevent the procurement of a potential disease present at the scene.

With the coming of the computer age, electronic death certificates have become available in some states. They have been based on the U.S. Death Certificate prototype. The top portion of the certificate is usually done with the aid of the family who can provide the necessary demographic material.

The following is the format used as a template for the death certificates throughout the United States. The system is undergoing a transition from paper format to electronic filing. The demographic portion completed with the assistance of the family. The "cause of death statement" is completed by the physician or coroner.

TYPE/PRINT IN PERMANENT BLACK INK FOR INSTRUCTIONS SEE OTHER SIDE AND HANDBOOK

LOCAL FILE NUMBER

U.S. STANDARD
CERTIFICATE OF DEATH

STATE FILE NUMBER

NAME OF DECEDENT: For use by physician or institution

SEE INSTRUCTIONS ON OTHER SIDE

NATIONAL CENTER FOR HEALTH STATISTICS — 1989 REVISION

DEPARTMENT OF HEALTH AND HUMAN SERVICES — PUBLIC HEALTH SERVICE

DECEDENT

1. DECEDENT'S NAME *(First, Middle, Last)*
2. SEX
3. DATE OF DEATH *(Month, Day, Year)*
4. SOCIAL SECURITY NUMBER
5a. AGE—Last Birthday *(Years)*
5b. UNDER 1 YEAR — Months / Days
5c. UNDER 1 DAY — Hours / Minutes
6. DATE OF BIRTH *(Month, Day, Year)*
7. BIRTHPLACE *(City and State or Foreign Country)*
8. WAS DECEDENT EVER IN U.S ARMED FORCES? *(Yes or no)*
9a. PLACE OF DEATH *(Check only one, see instructions on other side)* HOSPITAL: ☐ Inpatient ☐ ER/Outpatient ☐ DOA OTHER: ☐ Nursing Home ☐ Residence ☐ Other *(Specify)*
9b. FACILITY NAME *(If not institution, give street and number)*
9c. CITY, TOWN, OR LOCATION OF DEATH
9d. COUNTY OF DEATH
10. MARITAL STATUS Married, Never Married, Widowed, Divorced *(Specify)*
11. SURVIVING SPOUSE *(If wife, give maiden name)*
12a. DECEDENT'S USUAL OCCUPATION *(Give kind of work done during most of working life. Do not use retired.)*
12b. KIND OF BUSINESS/INDUSTRY
13a. RESIDENCE - STATE
13b. COUNTY
13c. CITY, TOWN, OR LOCATION
13d. STREET AND NUMBER
13e. INSIDE CITY LIMITS? *(Yes or no)*
13f. ZIP CODE
14. WAS DECEDENT OF HISPANIC ORIGIN? *(Specify No or Yes- If yes, specify Cuban, Mexican, Puerto Rican, etc.)* ☐ No ☐ Yes Specify
15. RACE—American Indian, Black, White, etc. *(Specify)*
16. DECEDENT'S EDUCATION *(Specify only highest grade completed)* Elementary/Secondary (0-12) / College (1-4 or 5+)

PARENTS

17. FATHER'S NAME *(First, Middle, Last)*
18. MOTHER'S NAME *(First, Middle, Maiden Surname)*

INFORMANT

19a. INFORMANT'S NAME *(Type/Print)*
19b. MAILING ADDRESS *(Street and Number or Rural Route Number, City or Town, State, Zip Code)*

DISPOSITION

SEE DEFINITION ON OTHER SIDE

20a. METHOD OF DISPOSITION ☐ Burial ☐ Cremation ☐ Removal from State ☐ Donation ☐ Other *(Specify)* _____
20b. PLACE OF DISPOSITION *(Name of cemetery, crematory, or other place)*
20c. LOCATION—City or Town, State
21a. SIGNATURE OF FUNERAL SERVICE LICENSEE OR PERSON ACTING AS SUCH
21b. LICENSE NUMBER *(of Licensee)*
22. NAME AND ADDRESS OF FACILITY

PRONOUNCING PHYSICIAN ONLY

Complete items 23a-c only when certifying physician is not available at time of death to certify cause of death.

23a. To the best of my knowledge, death occurred at the time, date, and place stated. Signature and Title ▶
23b. LICENSE NUMBER
23c. DATE SIGNED *(Month, Day, Year)*

ITEMS 24-26 MUST BE COMPLETED BY PERSON WHO PRONOUNCES DEATH

24. TIME OF DEATH M
25. DATE PRONOUNCED DEAD *(Month, Day, Year)*
26. WAS CASE REFERRED TO MEDICAL EXAMINER/CORONER? *(Yes or no)*

CAUSE OF DEATH

SEE INSTRUCTIONS ON OTHER SIDE

27. PART I. Enter the diseases, injuries, or complications that caused the death. Do not enter the mode of dying, such as cardiac or respiratory arrest, shock, or heart failure. List only one cause on each line.

Approximate Interval Between Onset and Death

IMMEDIATE CAUSE (Final disease or condition resulting in death) ➔ a. _____
DUE TO (OR AS A CONSEQUENCE OF):

Sequentially list conditions, if any, leading to immediate cause. Enter **UNDERLYING CAUSE** (Disease or injury that initiated events resulting in death) **LAST**
b. _____
DUE TO (OR AS A CONSEQUENCE OF):
c. _____
DUE TO (OR AS A CONSEQUENCE OF):
d. _____

PART II. Other significant conditions contributing to death but not resulting in the underlying cause given in Part I.

28a. WAS AN AUTOPSY PERFORMED? *(Yes or no)*
28b. WERE AUTOPSY FINDINGS AVAILABLE PRIOR TO COMPLETION OF CAUSE OF DEATH? *(Yes or no)*

29. MANNER OF DEATH ☐ Natural ☐ Accident ☐ Suicide ☐ Homicide ☐ Pending Investigation ☐ Could not be Determined
30a. DATE OF INJURY *(Month, Day, Year)*
30b. TIME OF INJURY M
30c. INJURY AT WORK? *(Yes or no)*
30d. DESCRIBE HOW INJURY OCCURRED
30e. PLACE OF INJURY—At home, farm, street, factory, office building, etc. *(Specify)*
30f. LOCATION *(Street and Number or Rural Route Number, City or Town, State)*

CERTIFIER

SEE DEFINITION ON OTHER SIDE

31a. CERTIFIER *(Check only one)*
☐ CERTIFYING PHYSICIAN *(Physician certifying cause of death when another physician has pronounced death and completed Item 23)* To the best of my knowledge, death occurred due to the cause(s) and manner as stated.
☐ PRONOUNCING AND CERTIFYING PHYSICIAN *(Physician both pronouncing death and certifying to cause of death)* To the best of my knowledge, death occurred at the time, date, and place, and due to the cause(s) and manner as stated.
☐ MEDICAL EXAMINER/CORONER On the basis of examination and/or investigation, in my opinion, death occurred at the time, date, and place, and due to the cause(s) and manner as stated.
31b. SIGNATURE AND TITLE OF CERTIFIER
31c. LICENSE NUMBER
31d. DATE SIGNED *(Month, Day, Year)*
32. NAME AND ADDRESS OF PERSON WHO COMPLETED CAUSE OF DEATH (ITEM 27) *(Type/Print)*

REGISTRAR

33. REGISTRAR'S SIGNATURE
34. DATE FILED *(Month, Day, Year)*

PHS-T-003

Figure 11.2 Electronic Death Certificate (Front)

INSTRUCTIONS FOR SELECTED ITEMS

Item 9. – Place of Death

If the death was pronounced in a hospital, check the box indicating the decedent's status at the institution (inpatient, emergency room/outpatient, or dead on arrival (DOA)). If death was pronounced elsewhere, check the box indicating whether pronouncement occurred at a nursing home, residence, or other location. If other is checked, specify where death was legally pronounced, such as a physician's office, the place where the accident occurred, or at work.

Items 13-a-f. – Residence of Decedent

Residence of the decedent is the place where he or she actually resided. This is not necessarily the same as "home State," or "legal residence." Never enter a temporary residence such as one used during a visit, business trip, or a vacation. Place of residence during a tour of military duty or during attendance at college is not considered as temporary and should be considered as the place of residence.

If a decedent had been living in a facility where an individual usually resides for a long period of time, such as a group home, mental institution, nursing home, penitentiary, or hospital for the chronically ill, report the location of that facility in items 13a through 13f.

If the decedent was an infant who never resided at home, the place of residence is that of the parent(s) or legal guardian. Do <u>not</u> use an acute care hospital's location as the place of residence for any infant.

Items 23 and 31 – Medical Certification

The PRONOUNCING PHYSICIAN is the person who determines that the decedent is legally dead but who was not in charge of the patient's care for the illness or condition which resulted in death. Items 23a through 23c are to be completed only when the physician responsible for completing the medical certification of cause of death (Item 27) is not available at time of death to certify cause of death. The pronouncing physician is responsible for completing only items 23 through 26.

The CERTIFYING PHYSICIAN is the person who determines the cause of death (Item 27). This box should be checked only in those cases when the person who is completing the medical certification of cause of death is <u>not</u> the person who pronounced death (Item 23). The certifying physician is responsible for completing items 27 through 32.

The PRONOUNCING AND CERTIFYING PHYSICIAN box should be checked when the same person is responsible for completing items 24 through 32, that is, when the same physician has both <u>pronounced</u> death and <u>certified</u> the cause of death. If this box is checked, items 23a through 23c should be left blank.

The MEDICAL EXAMINER/CORONER box should be checked when investigation is required by the Post Mortem Examination Act and the cause of death is completed by a medical examiner or coroner. The Medical Examiner/Coroner is responsible for completing items 24 through 32.

Item 27. – Cause of Death

The cause of death means the disease, abnormality, injury, or poisoning that caused the death, <u>not</u> the mode of dying, such as cardiac or respiratory arrest, shock, or heart failure.

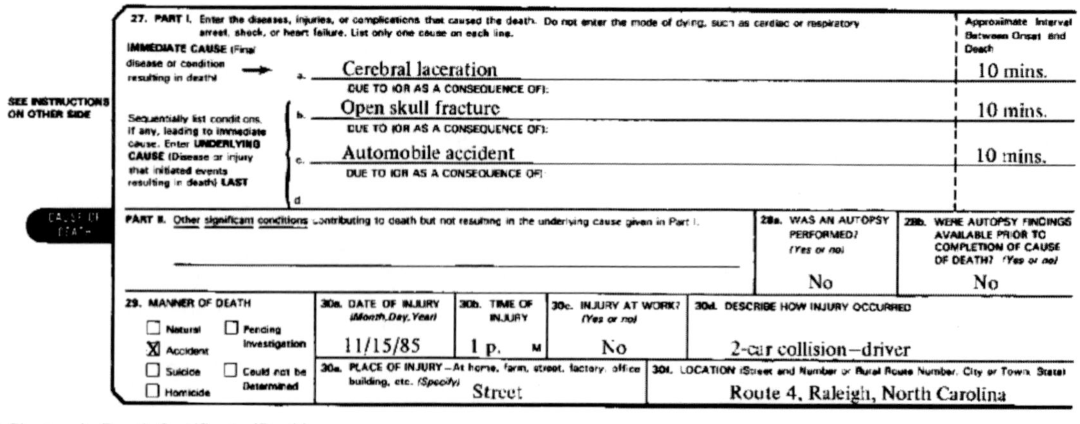

In <u>Part I</u>, the <u>immediate</u> cause of death is reported on line (a). Antecedent conditions, if any, which gave rise to the cause are reported on lines (b), (c), and (d). The underlying cause, should be reported on the last line used in Part I. No entry is necessary on lines (b), (c), and (d) if the immediate cause of death on line (a) describes completely the train of events. ONLY ONE CAUSE SHOULD BE ENTERED ON A LINE. Additional lines may be added if necessary. Provide the best estimate of the interval between the onset of each condition and death. Do not leave the interval blank; if unknown, so specify.

In <u>Part II</u>, enter other important diseases or conditions that may have contributed to death but did not result in the underlying cause of death given in Part I.

See examples below.

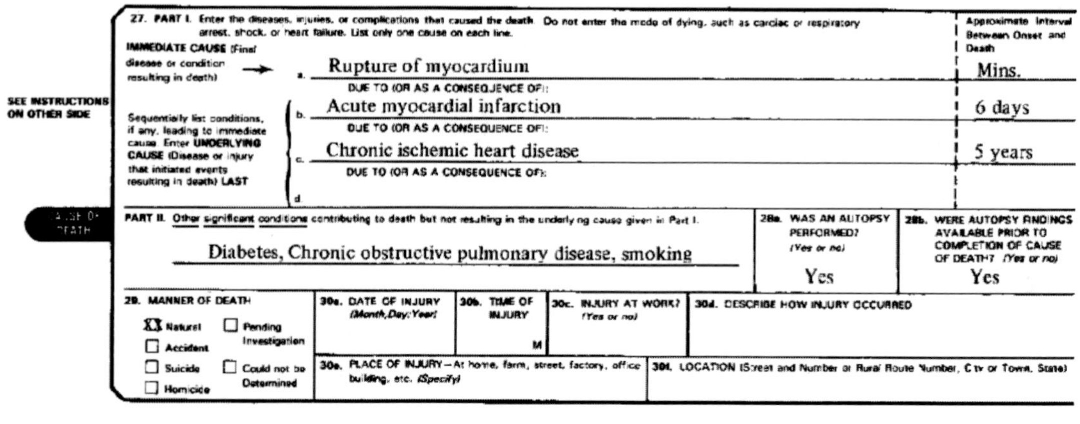

Figure 11.2 Electronic Death Certificate (Back)

CAUSE OF DEATH

The cause of death is the description used by the physician, and is based on disease processes. Examples are: Myocardial Infarction (heart attack), Atherosclerotic Cardiovascular Disease (hardening of the arteries), and Multiple Stab Wounds etc.

MANNER OF DEATH

The National Association of Medical Examiners makes the following distinctions between manners of death.[2]

Natural: Due solely or nearly totally to disease and/or the aging process.

Accident: There is little or no evidence that the injury or poisoning occurred with intent to harm or cause death. In essence, the fatal outcome was unintentional.

Suicide: Results from an injury or poisoning as a result of an intentional, self-inflicted act committed to do self-harm or cause the death of one's self.

Homicide: Occurs when death results from an injury or poisoning or from a volitional act committed by another person to cause fear, harm or death. Intent to cause death is a common element but is not required for classification as homicide.

Could not be determined: Used when the information pointing to one manner of death is no more compelling than one or more other competing manners of death when all available information is considered.

Pending investigation: Used when determination of manner depends on further information.

The manner of death assigned on the death certificate may be different than the one used by law enforcement or the judicial system. Even though a medical examiner/coroner may rule a death accidental, the judicial system may find enough evidence to charge someone with homicide or manslaughter. The criteria used by the judicial system are different than the medical system. An example is a motor vehicle accident where alcohol is involved. Law enforcement may feel there is enough to charge someone with vehicular homicide or manslaughter; the medical examiner may have ruled it accident based on the lack of intent to cause harm to another (bad judgment to drink and drive but no intent). The manner used by the medical examiner may not influence if charges are brought against someone.

FINGERPRINTING A DECEDENT

Fingerprinting a decedent is no different than fingerprinting a live person. The only difference is the decedent is not as easy to work with because of postmortem rigor. With death, the body begins to undergo a series of decomposition changes. The rigor causes the fingers to become stiff and less pliable which makes printing more difficult. The fingers are individually straightened and 'massaged' to loosen the rigor to accomplish the task more easily. All decedents need to be printed to verify identity. Medical examiners or coroners usually retain one set in their file to link a set of prints with a particular body. In some cases, identity might be disputed by family members or the prints may aid in the identification of a 'John/Jane Doe'.

In straightforward cases, prints of each of the fingers are usually sufficient. In homicide cases, a full set of fingerprints plus palms may be necessary. State laws usually require that a set of prints on all decedents be forwarded to the state police agency to run them through the AFIS database (automated fingerprint identification system). This purges the FBI's database of decedents and verifies identities.

Fingerprints are resilient even in decomposed bodies where the surface of the hand may have sloughed off with 'glove formation'. Prints can be obtained from the residual skin on the hands or the gloved skin can be used. The latter is done by placing the decedent's gloved skin over the printer's hand and rolling prints. (It may seem crude or even disgusting, but it is the best way). Sometimes, oily decomposition material may be present on the skin and a mild soap or rubbing alcohol can be used to cleanse the area before applying the fingerprint ink.

Other decomposition changes that result in challenges to obtaining good prints include drying and/or wrinkling of the skin. Wrinkled damp skin is easily dealt with by injecting the fingertips with formalin or even tap water using a syringe. The best area to insert the needle is at the first joint nearest the fingertip and directing the needle towards the tip of the finger but remaining in the deeper tissue. By gently instilling the fluid, the wrinkles can be removed and good, readable prints obtained. With dry, wrinkled skin, the process is more laborious and not as predictable to have a favorable outcome. If the hands are placed in water alone, they will soften but will decompose faster. Some offices have had success by placing the hands in a solution of dishwashing detergent to soften them then use the injecting technique to inflate the fingertips. Another method that has been used is a weak sodium hydroxide (lye) solution, which inflates the fingers by diffusion of the sodium into the skin. This method was found valuable by the author, but the fingers must be watched closely for over-processing. Lye is a caustic agent and must be handled carefully in addition to being one that can literally destroy the fingertips in hours and prints never obtained. When working with decomposition and attempting to obtain prints, it is best to print in stages and retain the best ones for comparison, even if they are obtained over a series of hours or days and on multiple cards.

X-RAYS

X-rays have the ability to penetrate the skin surface and give a view of the underlying anatomy and tissues. The view is made possible by the different densities possessed by different tissues and objects. Bone is denser than lung tissue and shows an outline on x-rays. Metal objects like bullets and knife tips are denser than bone and are readily evident. X-rays used in the realm of the autopsy are used to locate projectiles, knife tips, prostheses, broken bones, and for dental comparison.

IDENTIFICATION

Identification falls into two categories, presumptive (or circumstantial) and positive identification. Presumptive identification is based on wallets with identification cards, visual identification of a decedent, identification by tattoos or other characteristic marks etc. Positive identification is based on science and includes fingerprint comparison (there are no two prints alike except in twins), DNA identification, dental comparison and x-ray comparison. The previous order goes from most scientific to least scientific with DNA and prints being almost equal. The difference is the time delay and cost with DNA versus the ease, little cost, and short amount of time involved with fingerprint comparison. The drawback in all the scientific methods is the need for known exemplars to compare to from the decedent prior to death. Many people do not have prints on file and many states do not require a print on driver's licenses. Therefore, even if prints are obtained there may not be anything to compare to. The same is true of DNA and dental x-rays and bone x-rays. In these cases, it may be necessary to do presumptive identification based on the circumstances. The identification is left up to the medical examiner and the investigating police agency. If the decedent is found in their residence with no foul play and the description matches, then the presumptive identification may be sufficient. However, a decomposed body with multiple gunshot wounds found in a crack house or the middle of the desert requires a scientific work-up to determine the identity that will withstand judicial scrutiny.

SKELETAL REMAINS

Skeletal remains are defined as someone who has been reduced to bone with little or no soft tissue remaining. Decomposed remains are similar in that the decedent has undergone extensive postmortem change and this can range from bloating and discoloration to drying and mummification. Some may have artifacts secondary to animal activity, buried in graves or exposure to the elements. These present challenges including identification and determining cause and manner of death. Recovery of all the possible remains is imperative. This may require filtering dirt from a grave or surface soil through screens to locate small bones, bullets, personal effects, teeth or teeth restorations. Grave recovery will require special skills needed by trained investigators or the aid of a forensic anthropologist. To aid both identification and cause of death, x-rays of the submitted remains are usually the first order of business. They will locate projectiles, dental restorations and bone prostheses. Usually screening x-rays through the bag are done. After the recovery and cleaning of the bones, it may be necessary to x-ray them again to gather more detail and place them in anatomically correct positions. This will allow comparison to premortem (prior to death) x-rays. The anthropologist will also examine the bones for evidence of trauma, such as recent or old fractures. Possible instruments used to create the fractures, reconstruction of shattered skulls (either decomposed or fresh remains) may give information about weapons. An anthropologist can also give an estimate of age, sex and race based on the shapes of the skull and pelvis and stature based on the length of the femur.

Examination and photographs of clothing is important as it can aid comparison with missing person reports and give clues to the identity of the person. The clothing may even contain personal identification papers, laundry labels or money. Attention to details such as brand labels and size may add further information that needs to be documented in reports for later referral. Examination of the residual skin can give a clue as to race, tattoos and possible hair color. Any residual hairs should be gathered for possible DNA and should be photographed.

If teeth are present, a forensic dentist is called for consultation to aid in a positive identification. The dentist will examine the mouth, x-ray the oral cavity and chart the restorations onto a form that can be entered into a missing person's report. Teeth can also serve as a source of DNA. If the person has presumptive identification materials (a car left nearby, driver's license etc) that can be used to locate family and in turn dental records, the identification may be complete after the dentist examines the materials. Problems occur when the family has no knowledge of the dentist or medical records. Employers may have the information in their records from insurance claims and the pre-mortem dentist, physician or hospital may be located for medical records or x-rays.

When a family has a member go missing it is important that they gather all the medical information they can: hair brush with known hairs, toothbrush, dental x-rays and charts, medical records and medical x-rays. All this information is invaluable but difficult to obtain months or years later when hospitals have closed or they have purged their files. There has been interest in recent years to fingerprint children. This is an invaluable piece of identification that family members should retain. Is very difficult to identify children based on dental or bone comparison. If possible, the adults should also get printed and place the records in safe fireproof places. Holding DNA on each person is also valuable and is as simple as retaining some plucked hairs or some labeled dried blood on a small piece of clean cloth. In the era of mass disasters, this may be the only way to ensure their proper identification.

All the information on a Jane or John Doe is entered into a national database called the National Computer Information Center (NCIC).

UNIDENTIFIED PERSON WORKSHEET

Wisconsin Department of Justice
DJ-LE-278A (Rev 05/01)

UNIDENTIFIED CATEGORY

☐ Deceased

☐ Disaster Victim

☐ Living

ENTER	NCIC AGENCY IDENTIFIER	WI

Body Parts Status

Sex	Race	Estimated Year of Birth (Range)	Estimated Date of Death	Date Body/Person Found

Approximate Height (Range)	Approximate Weight (Range)	Eye Color	Hair Color

Scars, Marks, Tattoos, Etc.	Fingerprint Class

Agency Case Number	Blood Type	Circumcision	Footprints

Body X-Rays	Glasses

Cause of Death

Jewelry Type

Jewelry Description

Coroner and Case Number

Coroner Locality	Coroner Telephone Number

Miscellaneous

Operator	NCIC Number

CANCEL	NCIC AGENCY IDENTIFIER	WI

NCIC Number	Agency Case Number

Operator	Date Cancelled

Completed by:	Name	Verification	Date	Reason
Enter				
Modify				
Cancel				
Enter Supp.				
Cancel Supp.				

Figure 11.3 NCIC Unidentified Person Worksheet (Front)

UNIDENTIFIED PERSON WORKSHEET-Continued
DJ-LE-278A (Rev. 5.01)   Page 2

MODIFY	NCIC AGENCY IDENTIFIER	WI

NCIC Number	Agency Case Number	Operator

Body Parts Status

Sex	Race	Estimated Year of Birth (Range)	Estimated Date of Death	Date Body/Person Found

Approximate Height (Range)	Approximate Weight (Range)	Eye Color	Hair Color

Scars, Marks, Tattoos, Etc.	Fingerprint Class

Agency Case Number	Blood Type	Circumcision	Footprints

Body X-Rays	Glasses

Cause of Death

Jewelry Type

Jewelry Description

Coroner and Case Number

Coroner Locality	Coroner Telephone Number

Miscellaneous

ENTER SUPPLEMENTAL	NCIC AGENCY IDENTIFIER	WI

NCIC Number	Agency Case Number	Operator

Supplemental Scarmarks

CANCEL SUPPLEMENTAL	NCIC AGENCY IDENTIFIER	WI

System Identification Number	Agency Case Number	Operator

Supplemental Scarmarks

Figure 11.3 NCIC Unidentified Person Worksheet (Back)

1-694 (Rev. 10-12-94)

**MISSING PERSON REPORT
FOR NCIC RECORD ENTRY**

Date _____

Message Key (See definitions on page 1) (MKE)	Reporting Agency (ORI)	Name of Missing Person (NAM)
☐ Disability (EMD) ☐ Juvenile (EMJ) ☐ Endangered (EME) ☐ Victim (EMV) ☐ Involuntary (EMI) ☐ Caution		

Sex (SEX)	Race (RAC)	Place of Birth (POB)	Date of Birth (DOB)	Date of Emancipation (DOE)
☐ Male (M) ☐ Female (F)	☐ Asian or Pacific Islander (A) ☐ Unknown (U) ☐ Black (B) ☐ White (W) ☐ American Indian/Alaskan Native (I)			

Height (HGT)	Weight (WGT)	Eye Color (EYE)	Hair Color (HAI)	FBI Number (FBI)
		☐ Black (BLK) ☐ Hazel (HAZ) ☐ Blue (BLU) ☐ Maroon (MAR) ☐ Brown (BRO) ☐ Multicolored (MUL) ☐ Gray (GRY) ☐ Pink (PNK) ☐ Green (GRN) ☐ Unknown (XXX)	☐ Black (BLK) ☐ Brown (BRO) ☐ Blonde/Strawberry (BLN) ☐ Gray/Partially Gray (GRY) ☐ Red/Auburn (RED) ☐ White (WHI) ☐ Sandy (SDY) ☐ Unknown (XXX)	

Skin Tone (SKN)	Scars, marks, tattoos, and other characteristics (SMT) (See check list)	Fingerprint Classification* (FPC)
☐ Fair (FAR) ☐ Albino (ALB) ☐ Light (LGT) ☐ Olive (OLV) ☐ Black (BLK) ☐ Lt Brown (LBR) ☐ Ruddy (RUD) ☐ Dark (DRK) ☐ Medium (MED) ☐ Sallow (SAL) ☐ Dk Brown (DBR) ☐ Med Brown (MBR) ☐ Yellow (YEL)		

Other Identifying Numbers (MNU)	Social Security Number (SOC)	Operator's License Number (OLN)	Operator's License State (OLS)	Operator's License Year of Expiration (OLY)

Missing Person (MNP)	Date of Last Contact (DLC)	Originating Agency Case Number (OCA)	Miscellaneous (MIS) include build, handedness, any illness or diseases, clothing description, hair description, etc.
☐ Missing Person (MP) ☐ Catastrophe Victim (DV)			

Miscellaneous Information

Below is a list of clothing and personal effects. Please indicate those items the missing person was last seen wearing. Include style, type, size, color, condition, labels, or laundry markings. (MIS)

Item	Style/Type	Size	Color	Markings	Item	Style/Type	Size	Color	Markings
Head Gear					Shoes/Boots/Sneakers				
Scarf/Tie/Gloves					Underwear				
Coat/Jacket/Vest					Bra/Girdle/Slip				
Sweater					Stockings/Pantyhose				
Shirt/Blouse					Wallet/Purse				
Pants/Skirt					Money				
Belts/Suspenders					Glasses				
Socks					Other				

LICENSE PLATE AND VEHICLE INFORMATION

License Plate Number (LIC)	State (LIS)	Year Expires (LIY)	License Plate Type (LIT)

Vehicle Identification Number (VIN)	Year (VYR)	Make (VMA)	Model (VMO)	Style (VST)	Color (VCO)

Does the missing person have corrected vision? (SMT) ☐ Yes ☐ No ☐ Glasses ☐ Con Lenses	Has missing person ever donated blood? ☐ No ☐ Yes Where?	Has the missing person ever been fingerprinted? ☐ No ☐ Yes If so by whom?

Blood Type (BLT)	Circumcision (CRC)	Footprints Available (FPA)	Body X-Rays (BXR)
☐ A Positive (APOS) ☐ B Positive (BPOS) ☐ AB Positive (ABPOS) ☐ O Positive (OPOS) ☐ A Negative (ANEG) ☐ B Negative (BNEG) ☐ AB Negative (ABNEG) ☐ O Negative (ONEG) ☐ A Unknown (AUNK) ☐ B Unknown (BUNK) ☐ AB Unknown (ABUNK) ☐ O Unknown (OUNK)	☐ Was (C) ☐ Unknown (U) ☐ Was not (N)	☐ Yes (Y) ☐ No (N)	☐ Full (F) ☐ None (N) ☐ Partial (P)

Corrective Vision Prescription (VRX)	Jewelry Type (See check list) (JWT)	Jewelry Description (JWL)

Aliases	Reporting Agency Telephone Number	Reporting Officer

Complainant's Name	Complainant's Address	Complainant's Telephone Number

Relationship of Complainant to Missing Person	Missing Person's Address	Missing Person's Occupation (MIS)

NCIC Number (NIC)	Places missing person frequented (MIS)

Close friends/relatives	Possible destination (MIS)

Investigating Officer and Telephone Number (MIS)	Complainant's Signature	Date

* Submit fingerprints to the FBI CJIS Division, 10th and Pennsylvania Ave., Washington D.C. 20537

Figure 11.4 NCIC Missing Persons Format

Decedents are compared to known missing persons. The more scientific information available the better, as this narrows the number of potential matches and the results are more likely someone is to be identified. Fingerprints, dental charting and accurate stature information greatly aid the quest in identification. If families do not have the information available so that it can be entered in on the missing person, the match may not be made when an unknown person is found. The computer is only as good as accurate information is entered into the database both from the decedent portion and from the missing person component.

These two cases illustrate where identification would have been difficult had prints not been available:

1) A severed arm only was recovered from a dumpster. It was a female one with a small green-stoned ring. This was the only remains found after an extensive search. The family had reported their teenage daughter missing and she was wearing a green ring (presumptive identification). No prints were on file with the police but the family had a set in storage from when she was a child. A positive identification was made based on the comparison.

2) A young woman was reported missing after not returning from a rock concert. Her broken down car was found by the side of the interstate with a flat tire. There were no clues as to why she disappeared. Three years later, a young woman was found in a freezer in an adjacent state; bound by handcuffs, naked and beaten with a blunt object. Her fingertips were decomposing, but prints were obtained. Identification of her remains was rapidly made by their comparison with those present in the girl's prints in the NCIC missing person report and AFIS.

DISPOSITION OF UNKNOWN REMAINS

After a diligent search, sometimes decedents are unable to be identified. A diligent search includes running prints through the Automated Fingerprint Identification System (AFIS), entering an NCIC report in the national computer data base and following up on possible matches and talking to leads who reported people missing in the area (mountain trail, forest area etc). In recent years, the newspapers have been enlisted with descriptions of found persons who remain unidentified; this may generate leads, which need to be followed.

Clothing descriptions may also provide clues. Local missing person's reports may need to be reviewed. Some jurisdictions enlist the aid of facial reconstruction drawings or clay based on the bone structure of the skull.

Prior to someone being released for burial as an unknown person, screening x-rays of the entire body, DNA samples, head hair, photographs of all tattoos and clothing, dental x-rays and charting are verified. This ensures that proper screening can be done for later comparison if information should come forth rather than disinter someone from the gravesite for a comparison to be made. John/Jane Does should not be cremated in case the latter becomes necessary or the family wishes to claim the remains. Most state or local agencies have a public fiduciary branch, which can aid in the burial of the remains utilizing the person's assets or from public funds.

SUMMARY

In this chapter the importance of death certificates, cause and manner of death have been discussed. In addition, the aids used to identify unknown or skeletal remains including consultation services have been outlined. The differences between circumstantial or presumptive identification and positive identification have also been discussed.

DISCUSSION TOPICS

Vocabulary
- forensic anthropologist
- forensic odontologist
- NCIC
- AFIS
- CODIS
- cause of death
- manner of death
- death certificate
- skeletal remains
- prosthesis
- epidemiology

REVIEW QUESTIONS

1. List reasons why the NCIC database is not producing the results that it could and where the potential problems lie. (Note the reference below for further discussion)

2. Discuss how a forensic anthropologist can assist in the recovery of skeletal remains.

3. Discuss what information a forensic anthropologist can provide to aid in the identification of unknown remains.

4. What is the purpose of a death certificate?

5. List 5 causes of death.

6. List the 6 manners of death with a brief description of each. What is the major difference between the manners of death?

7. List items that constitute presumptive or circumstantial identification.

8. List items that constitute a positive identification.

9. Discuss the information that can be obtained from x-rays of a body.

10. Discuss the process of fingerprinting a body and the differences from a live person.

ADDITIONAL READING

Medical Examiners' and Coroners' Handbook on Death Registration and Fetal Death Reporting
www.cdc.gov/nchs/data/misc/hb_me.pdf

Medical Examiner and Coroner Information: Information on death investigation in the United States
www.cdc.gov/epo/dphsi/mecisp/methods.htm
www.cdc.gov/nchs/about/major/dvs/mortdata.htm

National Center for Health Statistics: Gives multiple links for causes of death, certification, and death statistics etc. NCIC forms for an unidentified person Information and report format for a missing person
www.doj.state.wi.us/DLES/CIB/forms/cib/djle278a.pdf
www.doj.state.wi.us/DLES/CIB/forms/time/missingPersonReport.pdf

This is a good series of articles about the problems of identifying the unknown. Shows statistics as to why people are missing and why they remain unidentified.
mpa.onemissingperson.org/
mpa.onemissingperson.org/NCIC_Overview.pdf

Missing person reports and dental identification through NCIC.
mpa.onemissingperson.org/20030226Missing_NCIC_Dental.pdf

ENDNOTES

1. http://www.chronography.com/death.html

2. Hanzlick R, Hunsaker JH III, Davis GJ. A guide for manner of death classification. St. Louis, Missouri: National Association of Medical Examiners. 2002. http://www.thename.org/Library/MannerRev.pdf. Jan 6, 2003

Chapter 12

Packaging and Transporting Evidence

OVERVIEW

This chapter covers the purpose, types of packaging, labeling, chain of custody and shipping of evidence.

CHAPTER OBJECTIVES

After studying this chapter, the student will be able to:

1. Understand the purpose of packaging evidence.

2. Understand the various primary and secondary packaging devices.

3. Understand basic methodologies for collecting various types of biological evidence.

4. Understand the procedure of labeling evidence packages.

5. Understand the purpose and importance of chain of custody procedures.

HISTORICAL PERSPECTIVES

The way evidence is packaged and the types of things that are collected have been greatly influenced by DNA evaluation capabilities. The OJ Simpson case has also affected how evidence is handled to prevent alleged contamination or inadmissibility.

PURPOSE OF PACKAGING

The purpose of packaging is to protect the evidence from contamination, breakage, degradation, mold or decomposition so it is not compromised for the purpose it was obtained. To prevent deterioration, the samples should be dried as soon as possible, placed in paper, not plastic bags (unless it is bone or tissue then it should be placed in plastic and frozen for preservation). All evidence should be stored in the freezer except tubes of blood (which will break if frozen) and these should be refrigerated.

TYPES OF PACKAGING

There are multiple types of packages available for evidence. The packaging provides a surface to label the evidence without affecting the contents. Evidence is usually collected in an initial primary package (filter paper, weighing paper, writing paper) then placed into a secondary package. The latter serves as a means to label the material, to seal with evidence tape and prevent loss or cross-contamination with the other collected evidence.

Paper Bags

Brown paper grocery bags are useful for large items such as clothing, sheets and other fabrics (Image 12.1). The paper allows the internal evidence to breathe and is especially useful if the evidence is damp. The top can be folded over and sealed with evidence tape (Image 12.2).

Image 12.1 Paper evidence bags are useful for clothing, sheets and other fabrics. (Permission for photograph from Lightning Powder Company)

**WARNING
SEALED EVIDENCE
DO NOT TAMPER**

**WARNING
SEALED EVIDENCE
DO NOT TAMPER**

Image 12.2 Evidence seals should close all pieces of evidence to ensure chain of custody. (Permission for photograph from Lightning Powder Company)

Paper Envelopes

Paper envelopes come in all sizes, from standard mailing size, to coin envelope, to manila envelope size. Some contain a clear portion so the internal contents can be viewed (Image 12.3). These are useful for handguns, small articles of clothing and trace evidence.

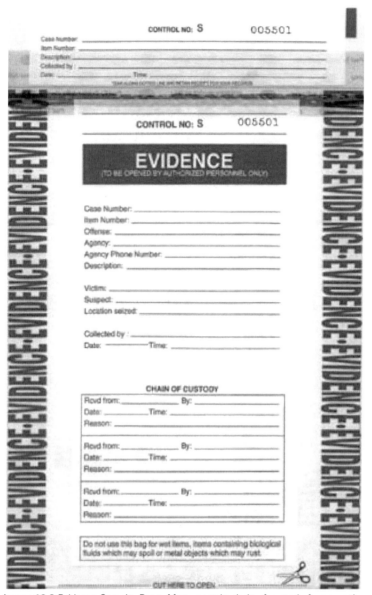

Image 12.3 Evidence Security Bags. Many contain chain of custody forms on the front and are partially composed of paper to allow breathing of the contents.
Source: Lightning Powder Company

Paper

Papers serve as a primary collection device. They easily hold trace evidence such as hairs, fibers and particles. The small pieces of evidence in paper are placed into a secondary package so as not to get lost in folds of envelopes. Filter papers and weighing papers are lightweight, cheap and of small size. To facilitate placement into the coin or mailing envelopes the conical, druggist or bindle folds may be useful (Images 12.4 -12.26). Any of these fold techniques will have the same result.

Conical paper fold

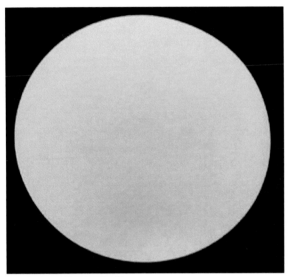

Image 12.4: Circular flat filter paper
Photo by Dennis Bucholtz

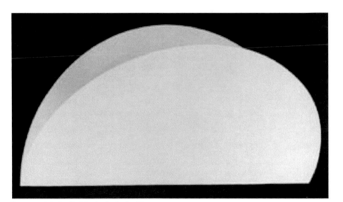

Image 12.5: Fold circle in half
Photo by Dennis Bucholtz

Image 12.6: Fold into quarter circle. Open center so 3 of the quarters form one side of the receptacle and the other ¼ the other side. Photo by Dennis Bucholtz

Image 12.7 Open the cone so it can serve as the primary collection device for small evidence.
Source - Personal collection: Ann Bucholtz)

Druggist paper fold

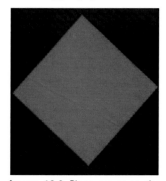

Image 12.8 Place paper on the diagonal.

Image 12.9 [Fold 1] Fold lower half over upper half, forming a triangle.

Image 12.10 [Fold 2] Fold the right 1/3 of the triangle toward the left.

Image 12.11 [Fold 3] Fold the left 1/3 of the triangle over fold 2.

Image 12.12 Slip fold 2 in between the two free edges of fold 3.

Image 12.13 This forms a small pouch at the top (between the layers) where you may place your trace evidence.

Image 12.14 Fold the top flap downward forming an envelope like closure.

Image 12.15 Slip the flap behind the free edge folds 2 & 3.

Image 12.16 Seal with evidence tape and place in an envelope.

Image 12.17 These simple, yet effective collection devices help prevent loss of small traces of evidence in folds or corners of regular envelopes. They are easily opened to reveal the entire containers contents.

Bindle paper fold: This fold can be used on square or rectangular paper

Image 12.18 This fold can be used on a square or rectangular paper.

Image 12.19 [Fold 1] Fold the right 1/3 of the paper toward the center.

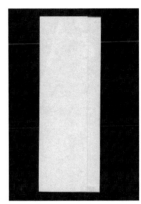

Image 12.20 [Fold 2] Fold the left 1/3 toward the center, overlapping fold 1.

Image 12.21 [Fold 3] Fold the lower 1/3 upward over folds 1 & 2 to about 1 inch from the top.

Image 12.22 This forms a top opening pouch where trace evidence may be placed.

Image 12.23 Fold top over and tuck the free edge into the crevice of the bottom fold.

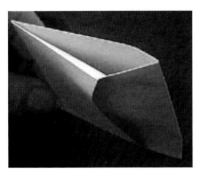

Image 12.24 Place evidence tape over the edge to secure the margins.

Image 12.25 Place the packet inside an envelope for marking and transport.

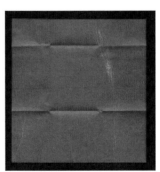

Image 12.26 After transporting, these envelopes are easily opened to reveal the entire containers contents.

Swabs

Swabs are usually supplied in sterile paper packages. After use, they will be moist and need to be dried or placed into breathable packaging (Image 12.27). Some kits contain collapsed small rectangular boxes large enough to fit one or two individual swabs.

Image 12.27 Swab & carton box (Permission for photograph from Lynn Peavey Company)

Sterile Containers

Sterile containers come in all sizes and are suitable for liquid specimens or protection of breakable specimens. Centrifuge tubes are great to transfer blood tubes in so as to prevent breakage or spillage. They are useful for packaging during mailing.

Specimen cups are larger and hold up to 300cc of fluid. The caps screw on and usually prevent leakage of the contents. They are useful for transporting tissue samples or urine.

Boxes

Specialty boxes are usually available to contain evidence that otherwise might be crushed or for protective reasons such as knives or guns. Clean unused pizza style boxes or specialty boxes made by evidence companies are available. Small slide style boxes may be useful for collection of smaller evidence like jewelry or bullets (Image 12.28).

Image 12.28: Small evidence box (Permission for photograph from Lynn Peavey Company)

COLLECTING EVIDENCE AT A SCENE

Overall, photographs of a scene from all angles are especially useful in later reconstruction of the crime for court or consultation purposes. Evidence can be marked with cone shaped numbers and the scene again photographed. Close-up photos of the evidence containing the number and a ruler are the best ways to document the evidence. The number is recorded on a log along with a short description of each piece of evidence for easy reference later.

Bloodstain Patterns

Bloodstain patterns can give valuable information concerning the type of actions that occurred at a scene such as a beating, gunshot wounds, instruments used etc. The pattern is best documented with photographs taken at a 90 degree angle from the surface and should include a ruler at the edge of the view field. The photographs should include overall photos containing a reference point (floor, piece of furniture etc) and close-ups of some of the droplets for directionality and velocity determination. Representative samples of the blood should be collected with a swab technique. Areas to be collected are circled with a pen and photographed for documentation.

Blood and Body Fluids

All specimens should be photographed before collection. These specimens are either wet or dry and are usually collected with swabs. If the sample is wet, a dry swab is used to absorb it. If the sample is dry, the swab needs to be dampened and the material collected followed by a second dry swab to absorb the specimen. After collection, both types of swabs need to be air dried and placed into an envelope for transport. Known standards of blood samples should also be obtained. Standards can be collected in purple top tubes or via finger stick onto a filter paper.

Clothing and Sheets

Prior to moving the item, it should be photographed as found. If trace evidence is adherent to the clothing that might be dislodged and lost, it should be collected into a conical or druggist fold and separately submitted in an envelope. The item should be gently folded on itself without shaking or holding it upward and placed into a brown paper bag. If it is damp with body fluids, it will need to be air-dried and packaged.

An evidence dryer is especially useful for this purpose and protects the evidence from cross contamination while it is drying (Image 12.29).

Image 12.29: Evidence drying cabinet to allow air-drying of clothing and other fabrics prior to storage. (Permission for photograph from Lightning Powder Company)

Hairs, Fibers and Miscellaneous Trace Evidence

Larger areas where trace evidence may be scattered but not easily seen can be retrieved using a small specialty vacuum cleaner device (Image 12.30). It has a small specialty filter, which can be submitted in its entirety to the lab for trace evaluation. These items should be gently collected with tweezers and placed into a druggist or conical fold. They are sealed into an envelope using tape and appropriately labeled. Collection of known standards of head hair, pubic hair and fibers should also be remembered.

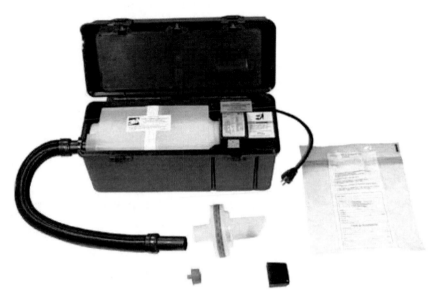

Image 12.30: Trace evidence vacuum to retrieve trace over a larger area. (Permission for photograph from Lightning Powder Company)

Paint/Glass

If the paint fragment is large, consider placing it into a small rigid container to prevent breakage. Glass can be placed in similar containers to prevent injury to personnel. For paint scrapings or smears, they can be processed by scraping them into a filter cone or druggist fold. These types of evidence may be procured from wounds of victims, especially hit and run motor vehicle accidents.

COLLECTION KITS

Sexual Assault Kit

These kits are usually prepared by a company to comply with each state's medical examination protocol. Each kit comes with the supplies and instructions to collect the necessary evidence for DNA analysis. There is one for a victim and one for a suspect. The victim one includes specimen procurement from all possible sites whereas the suspect one includes saliva, blood, pubic hair combings, head hair and pubic hair samples.

FAA Kit

These kits are prepared by the Federal Aviation Association and are to be used on the flight crew in an aircraft or other mass disaster. The kit contains all the necessary tubes and containers to fulfill the FAA evaluation requirements. Self-explanatory instructions are included in each shipping box.

DNA Kit

Blood is the specimen of choice and can be collected in purple top tubes or by finger stick onto filter paper (Image 12.31). Liquid blood should be transported refrigerated; blood dried on a filter paper can be easily transported and stored frozen. Other specimen kits are buccal swab kits (Image 12.32). These are advantageous as they are minimally invasive to the subject and easily collected. They involve using a swab or similar device to rub the inner cheek. The specimen needs to be air dried and frozen to best preserve the sample. A court order may be required.

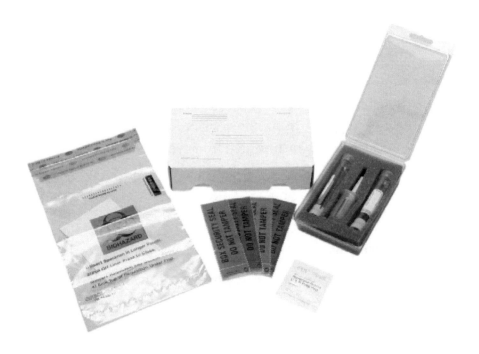

Image 12.31: DNA collection kit (Permission for photograph from Lynn Peavey Company)

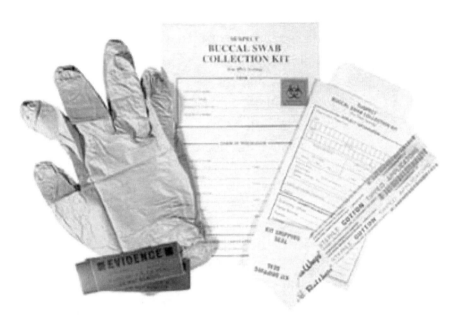

Image 12.32: Buccal swab kit (Permission for photograph from Lightning Powder Company)

Toxicology Kit

These are usually used for DUI or where drug testing of a live person is needed (Image 12.33). They include two gray top tubes and a container for submission of a urine sample.

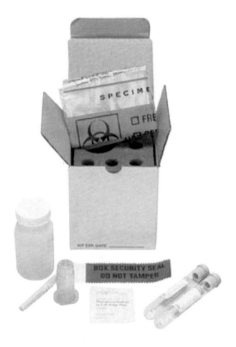

Image 12.33: Blood and urine collection kit for toxicology testing (Permission for photograph from Lynn Peavey Company)

LABELING OF PACKAGES

Evidence packages should be labeled with the following information using an indelible marker: (Image 12.34)

- The assigned case number
- Your name or initials
- Date and time of collection
- What is contained in the evidence package
- Location where the evidence was found
- Seal the container with evidence tape, initial and date the seal
- All evidence should be recorded on an evidence list

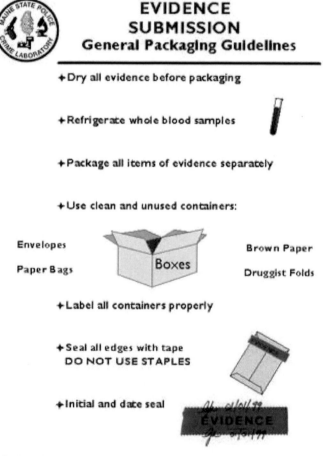

Image 12.34: Outline of proper collection of evidence and labeling of package.
From Maine State Crime Laboratory evidence handbook.

CHAIN OF CUSTODY

This procedure is defined as the documentation of the accountability for property or evidence. It is detailed with the type of evidence, time and date it was collected and signed for by all individuals who had possession of it and where it was secured. The purpose is to document proper storage and prevention of tampering or contamination. It also documents who performed testing and who collected it. This is important when presented in court during the evidentiary motions and admissibility as evidence.

Form 7: Chain of Custody Form

Name of juvenile _____

Signature of juvenile _____

Juvenile's I.D. # _____

Specimen collected by _____

Collection observed by _____

Date and time _____

For the analysis of _____

VERIFICATION, IDENTITY, AND CUSTODY OF THE SPECIMEN MAINTAINED BY:

Released By	Received By	Date/Time
_____	_____	_____
_____	_____	_____
_____	_____	_____
_____	_____	_____
_____	_____	_____

TO BE COMPLETED BY TESTING PERSONNEL ONLY

Seal broken by _____ Date/Time _____

Test performed by _____ Date/Time _____

Test verified by _____ Date/Time _____

Source: American Probation and Parole Association

Image 12.35 Chain of Custody Form

SHIPPING EVIDENCE

The best method to ship materials from one laboratory to another is to call the receiving laboratory for their requirements. They will usually have a standard operating procedure that will include times the evidence should be received and packaging requirements. Their request form for the desired type of service will also need to be included on the exterior of the package. It is best not to ship evidence overnight mail on a Friday as it will sit in a warehouse or loading dock over the weekend and may be compromised. Carriers such as FedEx, UPS and the US Postal Service all have their own requirements for shipping evidence and biohazardous materials. Evidence that needs to be shipped frozen will need to be packed on dry ice or with closed ice packs. Regular ice will leak and cause the evidence to be tossed because of leakage. Glass tubes, especially those containing blood should be packaged inside a container to prevent leakage (a centrifuge tube works well) then enclosed within another plastic bag marked with a biohazard symbol. Remember that shipping many times involves air travel of the specimen and expansion of liquids. Tubes will burst if overfilled. Styrofoam packing also protects the contents during automated sorting procedures and droppage.

The outside of the package needs to be clearly marked "Biohazard" and a biohazard sticker affixed. Other warning labels that may need to be attached are 'Glass', 'HIV or Hepatitis B Positive', 'Sharp', or 'Fragile'. The shipping label needs to be clearly marked with an indelible marker or printed label with permanent ink. Smeared addresses may not get delivered in a timely fashion or may be lost. Clear return addresses also need to be affixed. If it needs to be directed to a particular person or department that should also be indicated. Instructions for proper handling of the specimen should also be marked on the exterior, such as "Refrigerate upon arrival". The box should be marked 'evidence' and a proper chain of custody should be affixed externally so all persons handling it may sign and document its course without having to open the package.

When mailing evidence it is best to use certified mail or registered mail with return receipt. In general, the US Mail will not accept human tissue or body parts such as bones. Other carriers will have to be consulted on an individual basis for their regulations on biohazardous materials. In some cases, such as flammable materials, they will have to be delivered to the reference laboratory in person. Firearms may also pose a shipping problem and the carrier should be consulted, but in all cases, should be transported unloaded. Syringes are transported without needles or are placed into special sharps package containers (Image 12.36).

Image 12.36: Syringe tube for transporting needles and syringes safely to the laboratory.
Permission for photograph from Lightning Powder Company)

Figure 12.1 Investigative Tools and Equipment for Death Scene Investigator

1. Gloves (Universal Precautions)
2. Writing implements (pens, pencils, markers)
3. Body bags
4. Communication equipment (cell phone, pager, radio)
5. Flashlight
6. Body ID tags
7. Camera: 35mm (with extra batteries, film, etc.)
8. Investigative notebook (for scene notes, etc.)
9. Measurement instruments (tape measure, ruler, rolling measuring tape, etc.)
10. Official identification (for yourself)
11. Watch
12. Paper bags (for hands, feet, etc.)

Figure 12.1 Investigative Tools and Equipment for Death Scene Investigator (cont.)

13. Specimen containers (for evidence items and toxicology specimens)

14. Disinfectant (Universal Precautions)

15. Departmental scene forms

16. Camera—Polaroid (with extra film)

17. Blood collection tubes (syringes and needles)

18. Inventory lists (clothes, drugs, etc.)

19. Paper envelopes

20. Clean white linen sheet (stored in plastic bag)

21. Evidence tape

22. Business cards/office cards w/phone numbers

23. Foul-weather gear (raincoat, umbrella, etc.)

24. Medical equipment kit (scissors, forceps, tweezers, exposure suit, scalpel handle, blades, disposable syringe, large gauge needles, cotton-tipped swabs, etc.)

25. Phone listing (important phone numbers)

26. Tape or rubber bands

27. Disposable (paper) jumpsuits, hair covers, face shield, etc

28. Evidence seal (use with body bags/locks)

29. Pocketknife

30. Shoe-covers

31. Trace evidence kit (tape, etc.)

32. Waterless hand wash

33. Thermometer

34. Crime scene tape

35. First aid kit

36. Latent print kit

37. Local maps

38. Plastic trash bags

39. Gunshot residue analysis kits (SEM/EDS)

40. Photo placards (signage to ID case in photo)

41. Boots (for wet conditions, construction sites, etc.)

42. Hand lens (magnifying glass)

43. Portable electric area lighting

44. Barrier sheeting (to shield body/area from public view)

Figure 12.1 Investigative Tools and Equipment for Death Scene Investigator (cont.)

45. Purification mask (disposable)

46. Reflective vest

47. Tape recorder

48. Basic hand tools (bolt cutter, screwdrivers, hammer, shovel, trowel, paintbrushes)

49. Body bag locks (to secure body inside bag)

50. Camera—Video (with extra battery)

51. Personal comfort supplies (insect spray, sun screen, hat, etc.)

52. Presumptive blood test kit

(Source: Death Investigation: A Guide for the Scene Investigator

http://www.ncjrs.org/pdffiles/167568.pdf)

Figure 12.2 Crime Scene Equipment for the Crime Scene Investigator

1. Initial Responding Officer(s)

Essential:

- Consent/search forms
- Crime scene barricade tape
- First-aid kit
- Flares
- Flashlight and extra batteries
- Paper bags
- Personal protective equipment (PPE)

Optional:

- Audiotape recorder
- Camera with flash and extra film
- Chalk
- Directional marker/compass
- Disinfectant
- Maps
- Plastic bags
- Pocketknife
- Reflective vest

Figure 12.2 Crime Scene Equipment for the Crime Scene Investigator (cont.)

- Tape measure
- Tarps to protect evidence from the weather
- Traffic cones
- Waterless hand wash (towelette with germicide)
- Wireless phone

2. Crime Scene Investigator/Evidence Technician

Essential:

- Bindle paper
- Biohazard bags
- Body fluid collection kit
- Camera (35 mm) with flash/film/tripod
- Casting materials
- Consent/search forms
- Crime scene barricade tape
- Cutting instruments (knives, box cutter, scalpel, scissors)
- Directional marker/compass
- Disinfectant
- Evidence collection containers
- Evidence identifiers
- Evidence seals/tape
- First-aid kit
- Flashlight and extra batteries
- High-intensity lights
- Latent print kit
- Magnifying glass
- Measuring devices
- Permanent markers
- Personal protective equipment (PPE)
- Photographic scale (ruler)
- Presumptive blood test supplies
- Sketch paper
- Tool kit
- Tweezers/forceps

Optional:

- Audiotape recorder

Figure 12.2 Crime Scene Equipment for the Crime Scene Investigator (cont.)

- Bloodstain pattern examination kit
- Business cards
- Chalk
- Chemical enhancement supplies
- Entomology (insect) collection kit
- Extension cords
- Flares
- Forensic light source (alternate light source, UV lamp/laser, goggles)
- Generator
- Gunshot residue kit
- Laser trajectory kit
- Maps
- Marking paint/snow wax
- Metal detector
- Mirror
- Phone listing (important numbers)
- Privacy screens
- Protrusion rod set
- Reflective vest
- Refrigeration or cooling unit
- Respirators with filters
- Roll of string
- Rubber bands
- Sexual assault evidence collection kit (victim and suspect)
- Shoe print lifting equipment
- Templates (scene and human)
- Thermometer
- Traffic cones
- Trajectory rods
- Video recorder
- Wireless phone

Figure 12.2 Crime Scene Equipment for the Crime Scene Investigator (cont.)

3. Evidence Collection Kits (Examples)

Blood Collection:
- Bindle
- Coin envelopes
- Disposable scalpels
- Distilled water
- Ethanol
- Evidence identifiers
- Latex gloves
- Photographic ruler (ABFO scales)
- Presumptive chemicals
- Sterile gauze
- Sterile swabs
- Test tubes/test tube rack

Bloodstain Pattern Documentation:
- ABFO scales
- Calculator
- Laser pointer
- Permanent markers
- Protractor
- String
- Tape

Excavation:
- Cones/markers
- Evidence identifiers
- Metal detectors
- Paintbrushes
- Shovels/trowels
- Sifting screens
- String
- Weights
- Wooden/metal stakes

Fingerprints:
- Black and white film
- Brushes

Figure 12.2 Crime Scene Equipment for the Crime Scene Investigator (cont.)

- Chemical enhancement supplies
- Cyanoacrylate (super glue) wand/packets
- Flashlight
- Forensic light source
- Lift cards
- Lift tape
- Measurement scales
- One-to-one camera
- Powders

Impression:
- Bowls/mixing containers
- Boxes
- Dental stone (die stone)
- Evidence identifiers
- Measurement scales
- Permanent markers
- Snow print wax
- Water
- Pattern Print Lifter:
- Chemical enhancement supplies
- Electrostatic dust lifter
- Gel lifter
- Wide format lift tape

Toolmarks:
- Casting materials

Trace Evidence Collection:
- Acetate sheet protectors
- Bindle paper
- Clear tape/adhesive lift
- Flashlight (oblique lighting)
- Forceps/tweezers
- Glass vials
- Slides and slide mailers
- Trace evidence vacuum cleaner with disposable collection filters

Source: http://www.ncjrs.org/pdffiles1/nij/178280.pdf

SUMMARY

In this chapter you learned the importance of packaging, labeling, chain of custody and shipping of evidence.

DISCUSSION TOPICS

Vocabulary

- Primary collection package
- Secondary collection package
- Conical fold (filter paper)
- Druggist fold (weighing paper)
- Bindle fold
- Chain of Custody
- Biohazard seal

REVIEW QUESTIONS

1. Discuss the purposes of primary and secondary collection packages and the types of packaging that could be used for each.
2. List types of biological and physical evidence and what types of packaging might be best suited for each.
3. Outline the labeling procedure for an evidence package.
4. Describe the purpose and importance of chain of custody.
5. Outline shipping procedure guidelines for mailing an evidence package to a reference laboratory.

ADDITIONAL READING

Georgia State Crime Laboratory Requirements for Submitting Evidence
    www.state.ga.us/gbi/labmanual.html#5

Maine State Police Evidence Manual Outlining Collection and Submission Of Evidence Procedures.
    www.state.me.us/dps/msp/crimelab/evman.htm

Crime Scene Investigation: A Guide for Law Enforcement
    www.ncjrs.org/pdffiles1/nij/178280.pdf

Death Investigation: A Guide for the Scene Investigator
    www.ncjrs.org/pdffiles/167568.pdf

Biohazard Waste Containers and Procedures
    www.lbl.gov/ehs/Medical/html/biohazardous.htm

DNA and the OJ Simpson Case
    www.crimelibrary.com/criminal_mind/forensics/dna/
    1.html?sect=7

Chapter 13

DNA

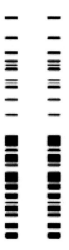

OVERVIEW

Knowledge of DNA is crucial to the understanding of the new forensic science laboratory and evidence collection. This chapter will cover the structure of DNA, how to collect specimens, pitfalls in testing and methodologies used in testing.

CHAPTER OBJECTIVES

After studying this chapter, the student will be able to:

1. Understand the structure of DNA and how it is utilized in DNA testing

2. Understand inclusion and exclusion terminology.

3. Understand collection of the DNA specimen and possible pitfalls.

4. Understand the principles of inheritance of nuclear and mitochondrial DNA.

5. Understand DNA typing, its relationship to cold cases and CODIS

HISTORICAL PERSPECTIVES

The structure of DNA forming the basis of life was published in 1953 by Drs. Watson and Crick. Science has been interested in DNA since that time in an attempt to understand the heredity of diseases, preventing disease, recombinant DNA, cloning and genetic engineering. Forensic science began using DNA as a method to identify sources of evidence in 1985 when Sir Alec Jeffreys discovered specific regions of the DNA code that made it possible to distinguish different individuals within the same species. The methodology allowed DNA to be considered as evidence via the ruling, Frye vs. United States, so that DNA is considered a substantiated scientific tool and admissible to court. Since then, the science has exploded. Technology has advanced to allow testing to occur with semi-automated instruments to speed up the turnaround time for results. DNA profiles of criminals from certain types of crimes (this varies from state to state but in general includes those convicted of murder, sexual assault and robbery) are now being entered into a central database within the FBI (Image 13.1). This library of possible suspects is then compared to DNA typing found at scenes and matches are being discovered. This fuels the fire to enter more data in an attempt to solve more cold cases and unsolved crimes. The other side of the coin also exists. Those unjustly incarcerated after being convicted of a crime may find means for appeal and release based on the absence of a match of their DNA to the evidence at a crime scene. Typically, they had been convicted based on the old ABO/HLA system or circumstantial evidence at the scene, which led to an unjust conviction. The database used by the FBI is called CODIS (Combined DNA Index System) and was first created in 1989.

DNA technology was used extensively on the World Trade Center victims of 9/11. Of the greater than 14,000 body parts, matches have been found in over 1400 of the nearly 2800 victims. (World Trade Center Forensics Breaks New Ground, Nature, April 23, 2003 by John Whitfield). DNA technology is also focusing on coding the DNA of deadly bacteria and other biological weapons as a means to trace their origin (anthrax outbreak, 2001).

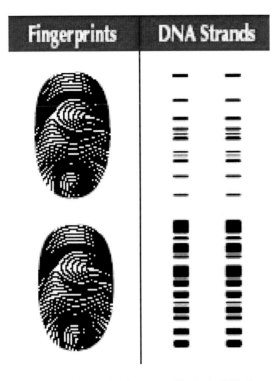

Image 13.1 DNA typing is as specific for individuals as fingerprints.

CHARACTERISTICS OF DNA

DNA stands for "deoxyribonucleic acid." It is a microscopic molecule and the backbone of chromosomes, our heredity system. Each person contains 46 chromosomes plus 2 sex chromosomes (2 X chromosomes denote a female; 1 X and 1Y denote a male). An individual inherits 23 chromosomes plus one sex chromosome from each parent. The only cells not having the complete DNA complement are the sex cells, i.e. the eggs and the sperm which each has half.

The DNA structure is called a double helix, the shape of a double parallel corkscrew. The sides of the corkscrew are formed by sugars and phosphates. Bridging the two edges are four base pairs, adenine, guanine, cytosine and tyrosine (Image 13.2). These bases arrange themselves so that guanine always pairs with cytosine and adenine always pairs with tyrosine. The sequence pattern of over 6 million of these bases is what makes each of us unique. DNA obviously has certain areas that are the same in all of us. We all have a gene sequence for hair, but whether it is curly or straight, light brown or black etc., is determined by unique sequence areas of the base pairs.

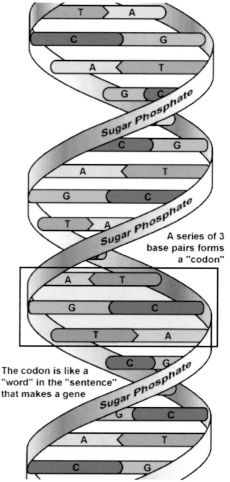

Image 13.2 label texts: "Sugar Phosphate", "A series of 3 base pairs forms a "codon"", "The codon is like a "word" in the "sentence" that makes a gene"

Image 13.2 Double helix structure of DNA connected by adenosine-tyrosine and guanine-cytosine base pairs

The same DNA is present in all cells of the body (except eggs and sperm). However, which parts of the sequence are turned on or off is determined by the cell and its function. DNA is a stable compound and does not change with age. The advantages of testing specimens for DNA rather than previously used ABO typing and serology testing are its greater specificity, its resistance to damage and it is more discriminatory for classifying specimens. Chromosomes are present in the nuclei of cells so only nucleated cells contain DNA. When testing blood, the red cells are without nuclei but the white cells contain DNA and this is the area targeted for analysis. Additional specimens include roots of hairs, sperm cells, epithelial cells such as buccal cells from the mouth, cells from the center of the tooth (dental pulp) and bone marrow (which is largely immature nucleated red and white blood cells). Less productive specimens are perspiration, tears, blood serum, liver and spleen tissue.

Table A-2. DNA Content of Biological Samples[336] and Genetic Testing Success Rates

Type of Sample	DNA Content	PCR Success Rate
Blood	20,000-40,000 ng/mL	
stain 1 cm x 1 cm	ca. 200 ng	>95%
stain 1 mm x 1 mm	ca. 2 ng	
Semen	150,000-300,000 ng/mL	
on post-coital vaginal swab	0-3000 ng	>95%
Saliva	1000-10,000 ng/mL	
on a cigarette butt	0-25 ng	50-75%
Hair		
root end of pulled hair	1-750 ng	>90%
root end of shed hair	1-12 ng	<20%
hair shaft	0.001-0.040 ng/cm	
Urine	1-20 ng/mL	
Skin Cells		
from socks, gloves or clothing repeatedly used		30-60%
from handled objects (e.g., a door knob)		<20%

Figure 13.1 DNA Content of Biological Samples and Genetic Testing Success Rates

The nuclear DNA base pairs are arranged so that there are short lengths that repeat themselves. These lengths vary in individuals and make each of us unique. They are called short tandem repeats. These are the areas currently used to determine the DNA typing of individuals. Currently, 13 areas are tested and their rate of occurrence in the population is known. This predictability is also used to establish the probability of a match when two specimens are tested for relationship to each other by comparison of these markers. DNA has the ability to discriminate samples to at least 1 in 6 billion or more.

DNA TESTING

There are two methods available to identify the DNA pattern in a sample; RFLP and STR techniques.

Restriction Fragment Length Polymorphism (RFLP) Techniques

Initially, DNA testing was done by Restriction Fragment Length Polymorphism techniques (RFLP). This technique utilizes a special enzyme called a restriction polymerase to cut the DNA at specific sites for the enzyme to create different fragment lengths of DNA. The different fragment lengths are characteristic for different individuals. The identification of the different lengths is done by gel electrophoresis, This is a laboratory procedure where an electric current is applied to a gel pad. The fragments are separated based on their size and charge. The resulting band pattern is visualized using markers that looks for a particular fragment (called a probe). This probe uses a radioactive technique called Southern Blotting. These fragment lengths can be quite long, somewhat cumbersome to work with and difficult to interpret. RFLP analysis requires a biological sample about the size of a quarter.

Short Tandem Repeats (STR) Techniques

It was discovered that DNA has another useful characteristic which can be capitalized upon to make statements about individuality of an evidence specimen. These are called short tandem repeats (STR's) which describes short segments of DNA repeating itself. These sequences are short and consist of 2 to 7 bases that can recur in a sequence up to 17 times. The particular sequence and length are characteristic from individual to individual. One set of sequence repeats is inherited from the mother on one chromosome and another set from the father (Figure 13.4 see notes at end). Additionally, it is this double number set that makes the sequence so individual. These sequences are targeted for copying by the Polymerase Chain Reaction (PCR). The STR technique has largely replaced the RFLP technique because it has greater accuracy and the short sequences are more resistant to degradation. In addition, the shorter sequences are easier to work with and utilize the copying technique with PCR.

The FBI has chosen 13 of these STR's to be included in the CODIS database to give a discriminatory power of two individuals having the same DNA pattern (except identical twins) of greater than 1 in 1 billion. These 13 probes (or loci) also allow standardization of the obtained data and different laboratories to enter them into the CODIS database.

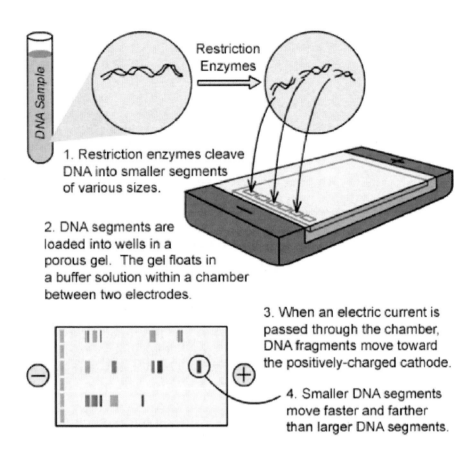

Image 13.4 Electrophoresis
Source: www.stanford.edu/group/hopes/diagnsis/gentest/s7.html

Polymerase Chain Reaction (PCR)

This method was first discussed in 1986 and is useful because it takes a small sample (a few cells) and reproduces certain areas of the DNA so that it is easily identified using probe technology. It takes a few copies of a particular desired sequence and makes more of them, similar to making copies in a copy machine. Because of this amplification process, it is imperative to prevent contamination by undesirable DNA, as that portion is also amplified. If a large amount of the undesired DNA is present, it can overwhelm the small sample size of the desired DNA.

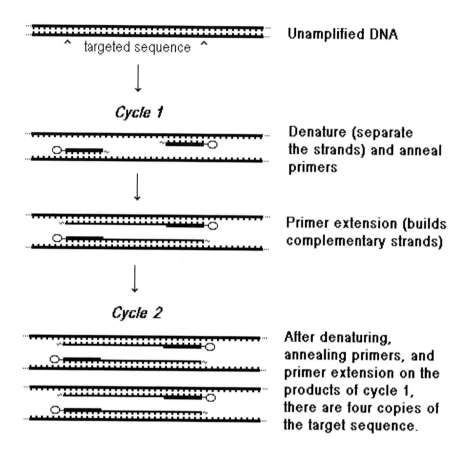

Image 13.5 The PCR Process

DNA Typing

The steps involved in the typing process are as follows:
- Extraction of the DNA
- Target certain areas of the DNA and amplify it
- Tag it with a marker so it can be detected
- Sort it by size
- Create the DNA profile using a variety of probes

Extraction of the DNA

The specimen is placed into a solution meant to release the DNA from the internal portion of the cell. This allows it to be manipulated in the following steps. As you remember, DNA is contained within the nucleus, which is contained within a nuclear membrane and a cell membrane. These portions of the cell can be broken down using detergent like materials, heat or agitation of the sample. The cell membranes are formed of phospholipids, a fat like substance. Just like detergent removes oil from our hands, it can do the same for removing the membrane from the cell. At this point, the solution is a mixture of free-floating DNA, cell fragments and detergent. The specimen is processed and the DNA is removed from the rest.

Target certain areas of the DNA and amplify it

This is accomplished using the Polymerase Chain Reaction. The locations of the short tandem repeats (STR's) are identified using special probes targeted for these areas. These areas are copied repeatedly to increase the sample amount (amplification).

Sorting the DNA

The DNA is a mixture of fragments at this point. The easiest way to separate the different pieces is by electrophoresis, which separates these molecular mixtures by charge and size. The process is based on the principle that all the pieces have a positive or negative charge. The mixture is placed on an agar gel on the negative side and an electric current is applied to the gel. The pieces with the negative charge move toward the positive terminal and the fragments with the positive charge move the smallest distance, remaining near the negative terminal. The smallest and most negative particles move the fastest toward the positive electrode. This in essence has separated the fragments based on their size.

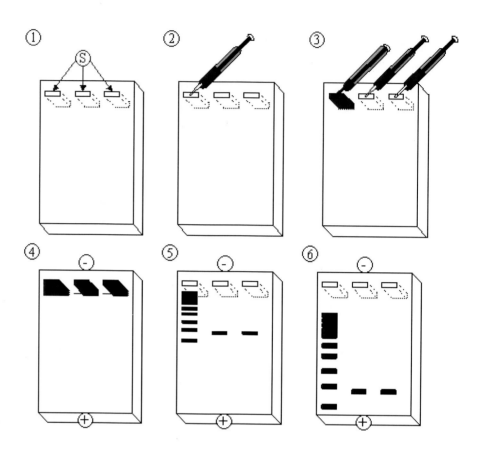

Image 13.6 Specimens are placed into wells near the negative charge (1 –3). The charge is applied and the mixture separates based on charge and size of the particles. The fastest moving negatively charged particles move fastest towards the positive electrode (4-5).

Creating the DNA Profile Using Probes

The bands are not visible to the naked eye so an indicator must be used to develop the gel. This can be in the form of radioactive particles, silver dyes or chemiluminescent dyes. Commonly, a fluorescent dye is used which is visible when the gel is exposed to a laser. The dyes are bound to particular band sequences, which bind to certain DNA fragments and cause a fluorescent glow. These are called probes and the term comes from the idea they are probing to see if that particular band sequence is present. The bands can be numerous depending on the number of probes (identifying markers) used. The gel can appear as a 'bar code' much as we see in grocery checkouts. This banding pattern is unique in each individual and forms the 'DNA profile' called DNA typing.

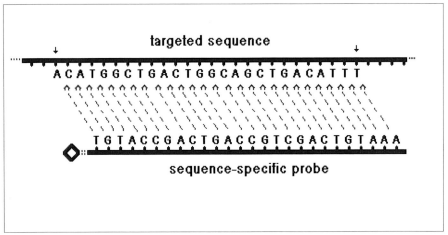

targeted sequence

A C A T G G C T G A C T G G C A G C T G A C A T T T

T G T A C C G A C T G A C C G T C G A C T G T A A A

sequence-specific probe

Image 13.7 A Sequence-specific probe links (hybridizes) to the targeted sequence on a single strand of DNA.

Interpretation

Each probe or tag has a known probability in the population. To perform a DNA profile anywhere from 4 to 13 probes is used each with a different probability of occurrence in the general population. By statistical methods, the probability of that occurrence is figured by multiplication of each of the individual probabilities. This is done based on a known mathematical phenomenon called the product rule. This states that the occurrence of a set of probabilities is the result of the product of each of them.

The suspect's probability of a match to suspect DNA is determined by a mathematical computation using the incidence of each loci present. The loci probability are a known value that has been established as part of it's uniqueness to determine individuality of one person from another. The suspect's uniqueness is then compared to the evidence.

DNA Probe	**Type**	**Suspect**	**Incidence in Population**
Locus	@ scene	SMITH	
1	BB	BB	5%
2	zz	zz	1%
3	LL	LL	10%
4	cc	cc	8%
5	mm	mm	6%

Figure 13.2 Incidence of Loci. Based on DNA profile Suspect Smith is not excluded. Multiplying the incidence of these 5 loci results in probability 1 in 5 million that it is Mr. Smith and no one else who could have left this DNA type at the scene.

TERMINOLOGY USED

Exclusion

If the DNA from a suspect is excluded, it means that the DNA present in the unknown sample has no loci or sites in common with the suspect. It is important that the sample site be taken into account. If a sexual assault kit is negative for the suspect's DNA type in the vaginal sample of a victim, it does not mean that he is no longer a suspect if other evidence links him to the scene. He could have been wearing a condom or did not penetrate the vagina.

Inclusion

If a suspect's DNA profile is included, it means that their DNA profile is consistent with the evidence at the scene. The strength of the evidence rests on the number of loci tested and the probability of that match occurring somewhere else in the general population. Hence, the overall probability of the DNA profile is crucial in proving that a piece of evidence came from that suspect. Usually, the profile is proven by utilizing a number of markers to a probability of one in millions or billions. This is enough to prove beyond a reasonable doubt that the suspect was the source of the DNA. Whether they committed the 'crime' is another matter. There may be another reasonable conclusion as to why their DNA is present at the scene. An example is sexual assault. A husband's DNA may be present in the sample along with another suspect's. Both DNA profiles would need to be done to exclude the husband's loci from the sample.

Inconclusive

This term means that the DNA sample has neither included nor excluded the person as the source of the sample. This could be because the sample was too degraded, there was too little of the sample to evaluate it or it was contaminated.

COLLECTION OF DNA EVIDENCE

Because DNA can be done on very small sample sizes, almost any object at a crime scene may yield results. The transfer of DNA occurs whenever any object comes into contact with skin, hair, or body secretions. Possible sources are: hats, clothing, cigarettes, fingernail scrapings, condoms, glasses, bottles, cans, envelopes etc). A particular piece of evidence at a crime scene and its relevance to solving a crime is usually not apparent. It is better to collect everything that has even the remotest possibility of relationship than to wish for it later.

Evidence	Possible Location of DNA on the Evidence	Source of DNA
Baseball bat or similar weapon	Handle, end	Sweat, skin, blood, tissue
Hat, bandanna or mask	Inside	Sweat, hair, dandruff
Eyeglasses	Nose or ear pieces, lens	Sweat, skin
Facial tissue, cotton swab	Surface area	Mucus, blood, sweat, semen, ear wax
Dirty laundry	Surface area	Blood, sweat, semen
Toothpick	Tips	Saliva
Used cigarette	Cigarette butt	Saliva
Stamp or envelope	Licked area	Saliva
Tape or ligature	Inside/outside surface	Skin, sweat
Bottle, can or glass	Sides, mouthpiece	Saliva, sweat
Used condom	Inside/outside surface	Semen, vaginal or rectal cells
Blanket, pillow, sheet	Surface area	Sweat, hair, semen, urine, saliva
"Through & through" bullet	Outside surface	Blood, tissue
Bite mark	Person's skin or clothing	Saliva
Fingernail, partial fingernail	Scrapings	Blood, sweat, tissue

Figure 13.3 Potential sources of DNA in evidence.

When collecting DNA evidence it is best to use the following precautions:

- Change gloves often
- Use disposable instruments or clean them thoroughly and often to prevent cross-contamination
- Avoid touching, talking, coughing or sneezing over an area where DNA evidence may exist (wear a mask)
- Avoid touching any clothing or your face with your gloves on (maintain clean technique)
- Air dry evidence thoroughly
- Put evidence in paper bags, sample containers or envelopes. Do not use plastic.

When transporting evidence, it is important to keep it dry and at room temperature. Do not keep it in the sun or in the back of a van or car.

Elimination samples may be necessary. These are samples taken from known people at the scene so their DNA can be eliminated as coming from the potential suspect. Elimination samples include people who normally live in a house, the owner of a car, the known victim or decedent.

Problems with DNA Samples

Probably the biggest problem with DNA samples is contamination of the sample. If the DNA is present in a small amount, it can be overwhelmed by contamination and unable to be pulled out of the specimen to be identified. This is made worse by the amplification process. The contaminating DNA is amplified just as much as the sample you are seeking.

DNA contamination can occur not only from the surrounding environment, but also by the people who collect it or by the people who enter a scene and contaminate it with 'foreign material'. Scene investigations require self-surveillance to prevent this from happening. Disposable jumpsuits, shoe covers and hair covers are used routinely. Disposable gloves are used not only to prevent leaving false fingerprints but also to prevent leaving false DNA. To prevent cross-contamination between areas, it is important to change gloves frequently. If in doubt whether you are contaminated, it is better to take the time to change gloves, shoe covers or whatever to prevent problems down the line during laboratory analysis or interpretation of the results.

All living organisms have DNA; this includes bacteria. If specimens are not dried properly, the wet environment of the sample proves to be a prime culture media for the growth of bacteria and mold, which can overwhelm and destroy the sample.

DNA is somewhat resistant to heat degradation and samples can be obtained in severely burned bodies. These specimens will prove better if obtained from the bone or areas removed from surface exposure to the heat.

Severely decomposed bodies are bacteria factories. Blood specimens and internal organs degrade and may not be suitable for DNA analysis because of bacterial overgrowth. Bone specimens may prove to be more profitable sites to sample as the bone marrow is contained within the thick covering of the bone surface and resistant to migration of bacteria. It is important to protect the specimen from contamination by the overlying putrefied tissue during DNA collection. PCR technology has improved the return on testing of degraded specimens. Larger fragments of DNA are affected more than the smaller ones.

Saying all this, DNA is relatively resistant to degradation. Samples contaminated with motor oil, gasoline, acids and alkalis have been recovered.[4] The internal portions of teeth (the pulp) proves to be another site suitable for testing of DNA even in difficult circumstances such as skeletal remains, severely burned bodies or in cases of extreme mutilation (World Trade Center, 9/11). Teeth are resistant to burning or trauma and are easily identified when found. Bacteria can seriously damage or degrade DNA contained in biological material and inhibit the ability to develop a DNA profile; however, evidence can still sometimes yield DNA results. For example, PCR technology can allow the laboratory to develop profiles from some moldy biological samples, whereas other evidence may fail to yield a usable DNA profile, even when no mold is visible. Therefore, close consultation with the laboratory is important.

Mitochondrial DNA (mDNA)

DNA technology has progressed rapidly since testing has become available. With the PCR technology, it has become possible to test very small specimens. DNA profiling is possible even on a single hair shaft containing a root. It will soon become automated to the point that it is as routine as testing blood for electrolytes or hematocrit.

There are instances (decomposition, heat, skeletal remains or degradation of the specimen) that cause the nuclear DNA to be unusable. It was known that the mitochondria, small organelles within the cell's cytoplasm, contained small circular fragments of DNA. To distinguish this DNA from the more commonly used nuclear DNA, it is called mitochondrial DNA. This DNA is unique in that it is only inherited from the maternal side. So all relatives with the same maternal lineage will have related mitochondrial DNA. This principle is useful in cases where the traditional maternal (mother) and paternal (father) nuclear DNA testing is not possible; for example, the mother and or father are both dead or unknown (adopted) but a sibling is available. Mitochondrial

DNA has the added advantage of being able to be done on very small specimens because there are many mitochondria per cell vs. only one nucleus. It is estimated that each cell contains between 1000 and 10000 copies of mitochondrial DNA.[1]

The circular structure makes it more resistant to degradation. So why isn't it done on all specimens? It is more costly and time consuming to isolate and perform. mDNA is not a positive means of identification because all maternal relatives have the potential to share the same profile. It is used as an adjunct to investigation and to narrow the likelihood that it is someone else.

Recombinant DNA

Recombinant DNA is a rapidly growing area in DNA technology. At this point, it does not have forensic implications but is important in the medical and scientific field. It is a process where a desired piece of DNA is inserted into a vector (usually a microorganism such as E.coli) where the organism works as the factory to produce the DNA product, a protein. The proteins that can be produced include Human insulin, vaccine for Hepatitis B and human clotting factors.

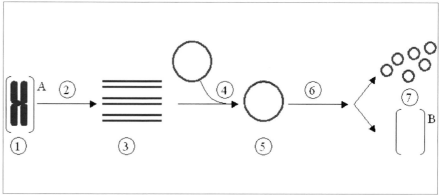

Image 13.10 Recombinant DNA technology. (1) Chromosomal DNA of organism A. (2) PCR. (3) Multiple copies of a single gene from organism A. (4) Insertion of the gene into a plasmid. (5) Plasmid with gene from organism A. (6) Insertion of the plasmid in organism B. (7) Multiplication or expression of the gene, originally from organism A, occurring in organism B.
(Source: http://en.wikipedia.org/wiki/Polymerase_chain_reaction)

Cloning

Cloning has made headlines and also has no forensic applications at this time. Cloning is the procedure of taking the entire genetic makeup of one organism and creating an exact same organism from that DNA. Scientists have learned how to manipulate the DNA and improve the organism, creating an organism that is superior in some fashion to the parent organism (genetic engineering). An example is a plant that is susceptible to a disease. With genetic engineering, it is possible to alter the plant's DNA and breed plants that are resistant to the disease. Stem cells are the primitive foundation cells of an organism and are the target cells where the manipulation of animal DNA occurs.

DNA and Identical Twins

At conception, an egg and sperm combine to form a zygote. In these early stages of development, the organism is composed of a few hundred cells. Sometimes during these early development stages, the zygote divides into two equal portions forming twins. When the development continues, each twin will have the same identical DNA content. DNA profiling of each will reveal the same profile and they cannot be distinguished.

Not all twins are identical; some are fraternal twins and result when two eggs are fertilized by two sperms at the same time. This results in two different zygotes with two different DNA profiles. It is just coincidental that the siblings were conceived at the same time. Their DNA profiles are distinguishable just as if they were two separate siblings.

Y-Chromosome Analysis

Several genetic markers have been identified on the Y chromosome that can be used in forensic applications. Y-chromosome markers target only the male fraction of a biological sample. Therefore, this technique can be very valuable if the laboratory detects complex mixtures (multiple male contributors) within a biological evidence sample. Because the Y chromosome is transmitted directly from a father to all of his sons, it can also be used to trace family relationships among males. Advancements in Y-chromosome testing may eventually eliminate the need for laboratories to extract and separate semen and vaginal cells (for example, from a vaginal swab of a rape kit) prior to analysis[2].

CODIS (Combined DNA Index System)

Currently, RFLP and mDNA profiles are not compatible with the convicted offender or forensic indexes of CODIS and only STR types are able to be included. CODIS is a computer software program that operates local, state, and national databases of DNA profiles from convicted offenders, unsolved crime scene evidence, and missing persons. Every State in the Nation has a statutory provision for the establishment of a DNA database that allows for the collection of DNA profiles from offenders convicted of particular crimes. CODIS software enables state, local and national law enforcement crime laboratories to compare DNA profiles electronically, thereby linking serial crimes to each other and identifying suspects by matching DNA profiles from crime scenes with profiles from convicted offenders. CODIS uses two indexes to generate investigative leads in crimes for which biological evidence is recovered from a crime scene. The convicted offender index contains DNA profiles of individuals convicted of certain crimes ranging from certain misdemeanors to sexual assault and murder. Each state has different "qualifying offenses" for which persons convicted of them must submit a biological sample for inclusion in the DNA database. The forensic index contains DNA profiles obtained from crime scene evidence, such as semen, saliva or blood. CODIS uses computer software to automatically search across these indexes for a potential match.

The missing person's index consists of the unidentified person's index and the reference index. The unidentified person's index contains DNA profiles from recovered remains, such as blood, bone, teeth, or hair. The reference index contains DNA profiles from related individuals of missing persons so that they can be periodically compared to the unidentified person's index. All samples for this index are typed using mDNA and STR DNA analysis (if possible).

Admissibility in Court

As with any new scientific technique, it must be proven that the scientific method is sound and within the scope of proven medical or scientific science. When DNA was initially introduced to the forensic and judicial community, it too had to pass this scientific challenge. In Frye vs. United States, this is a four point challenge. The evidence is relevant to the case; the evidence must be based on generally accepted scientific practice; the witness is qualified as an expert witness; and the expert is qualified to express opinions about the evidence. In some states the Frye test for admissibility has been replaced by the Supreme Court decision of Daubert vs. Merrill Dow Pharmaceuticals which established that it should be reliable, relevant, grounded on scientific validity based on methodology, not just conclusions. The judge serves as the "gatekeeper" for this expert testimony.

Post Conviction Cases

Because cases before the early 1990s were based on ABO and HLA typing, some individuals were improperly incarcerated because the evidence was not as strong as we are now able to prove. However, DNA is resistant to deterioration and these cases may be retested upon appeal. PCR technology may assist in proving the subject was involved, exclude them or the results may be inconclusive. The converse is also true. Those cases, which have turned cold or unsolved, may be solved with this new technology. Suspects may be linked based on little evidence or thru the CODIS system by offering evidence between cases, across jurisdictions and across state lines.

Cold Case Files

When properly documented, collected, and stored, biological evidence can be analyzed to produce a reliable DNA profile years, even decades, after it is collected. Just as evidence collected from a crime that occurred yesterday can be analyzed for DNA, today evidence from an old rape kit, bloody shirt or stained bedclothes may contain a valuable DNA profile. These new analysis techniques, in combination with an evolving database system, make powerful arguments for the reevaluation of unsolved crimes for potential DNA evidence. Knowledgeable law enforcement officers are taking advantage of DNA analysis techniques by investigating crime scenes with a keener eye toward biological evidence. The same new approach being applied to crime scene processing and current case investigation can be applied to older unsolved cases. Law enforcement agencies across the country are establishing cold-case squads to systematically review old cases for DNA and other new leads.[3]

Statutes of limitation may be one of the most difficult issues to overcome when examining older cases. Statutes of limitation establish time limits under which criminal charges can be filed for a particular offense. These statutes are rooted in the protection of individuals from the use of evidence that becomes less reliable over time. DNA evidence has the power to determine truth 10, 15, even 20 years after an offense is committed. States are beginning to realize that the reliability of DNA technology may necessitate the reevaluation of statutes of limitation in the filing of cases. The effectiveness of the DNA database relies on the volume of data contained in both the forensic index (crime scene samples) and the convicted offender index of CODIS. Many states are changing their database statutes to include less violent criminals and to require all convicted felons to submit a DNA profile. The tendency for states to include all convicted felons in their databases dramatically increases the number of convicted offender DNA profiles against which forensic DNA evidence can be compared, thus making the database system a more powerful tool for law enforcement.

Article 13.1 Sample Handling Considerations for Biological Evidence and DNA Extracts

Sample Handling Considerations for Biological Evidence and DNA Extracts

Theresa F. Spear
California Department of Justice
California Criminalistics Institute

Introduction

This article will make recommendations for handling biological evidence from sample collection to sample storage. Depending upon the type of biological evidence, it may be very difficult to detect certain types of samples. Saliva and semen stains are often not visible. Even bloodstains may be difficult to find if they are on a dark substrate. Although specialized, forensic light sources are sometimes helpful in visualizing these stains, they cannot always be relied upon to find all biological stains. It is especially difficult to detect saliva or semen on some dark colored fabric with any of the widely used forensic light sources. Thus, a stereomicroscope or chemical mapping techniques may be required to improve the chances of finding all biological evidence. After a sample has been detected, steps must be taken to insure that the sample integrity is maintained and the chances of contamination are minimized.

Sample Collection in the Field

Once a sample has been located and a decision has been made to take the sample, issues arise as to how to collect, dry and package it for transportation to the laboratory. Considerations relevant at this stage include the ability to obtain as much sample as possible, to minimize degradation and finally to insure that samples are not inadvertently contaminated with other biological samples.

Article 13.1 Sample Handling Considerations for Biological Evidence and DNA Extracts (cont.)

The standard recommendation for collecting biological evidence is *not* to remove the stain from an object, but rather to collect the object with the stain. The advantages of this strategy are that the entire stain is obtained, it is not necessary to collect an "unstained control" sample and there are no further manipulations required that might negatively impact the sample. If the stain is on a smooth, non-porous surface (i.e. it can be easily "flaked" off), it will be necessary to protect the stain from contact with other objects. Depending upon the nature of the evidence, a stain can be protected by immobilizing the evidence item in a cardboard box (e.g., with pieces of wire) or by taping a piece of paper over the stain (if this will not destroy other evidence, such as fingerprints). *Provided that the stain can be adequately protected, this is the optimum collection procedure.*

Given that some stains are found on immovable objects, it is not always possible to collect the object with the stain. Some samples will need to be collected in the field. If the entire object cannot be collected then *the next best way to collect biological evidence is to remove the stain by cutting it out (e.g., from a piece of carpet).* Remember to use clean scissors and to cut out an "unstained" control. Scissors or tweezers can be cleaned by rinsing with clean water and then drying with tissue. Repeat this cleaning process twice prior to each sampling.

It is not necessary to clean tools with bleach. Improperly used, bleach could destroy biological evidence.

There will be occasions when it is not possible to collect a stain by cutting it from an object (e.g., a stain on a concrete floor). The two methods traditionally used to collect these stains are: (1) to use a dampened cotton swab, thread or piece of gauze to collect the stain or (2) to use a clean implement (e.g., razor blade) to scrape the stain into a clean paper bindle. *With these two methods, it will typically be necessary to take an "unstained" control sample.* Scraping is practical only when the *stain is in the form of a crust* and it can be

Article 13.1 Sample Handling Considerations for Biological Evidence and DNA Extracts (cont.)

lifted from a smooth, non-porous surface. The most significant problem encountered while scraping stains is that samples tend to "powder" when scraped and it may be difficult to control the retrieval of the entire sample. The "powdered" stain, which is not retrieved, may contaminate adjacent stains. Given these considerations, most samples will not lend themselves to the scraping technique and will need to be collected by swabbing.

The best method for swabbing a stain is to use a minimum amount of distilled water to dampen an appropriate, clean substrate (e.g., cotton swab or cotton gauze) and then absorb the stain onto the slightly dampened substrate. An unstained control is taken in the same manner as the stain and is taken from an unstained area as close as possible to the biological evidence sample. It may be useful to test the "unstained" area with an appropriate presumptive test to see if it contains a biological sample. In an effort to keep the stain as concentrated as possible, the size of substrate used to absorb the stain is important. Ideally, the smaller the stain, the smaller the substrate used to collect that stain. Thus one might choose to use a small piece of cotton gauze rather than a swab to collect a small blood spatter (1 or 2 mm in diameter). In order to protect the integrity of a small sample, the dampened gauze should only be handled with clean tweezers. If a stain is not very small, *swabs are probably easiest to use* since they do not require the use of tweezers or any other intermediate object.

Cotton swabs have traditionally been used to collect biological samples. They are readily available in sterile packages and they are very absorbent. Do *not* use "calcium alginate" swabs for sample collection since these swabs interfere with many of the DNA extraction procedures. Cotton gauze, which does not have any additive (e.g., fabric sizing), is also an acceptable substrate.

Once a stain is collected, the next consideration is drying the swabbed sample. Drying biological samples is critical to preserving these samples because water is necessary in most of the biochemical

Article 13.1 Sample Handling Considerations for Biological Evidence and DNA Extracts (cont.)

reactions that result in degradation. Try to dry this sample as fast as possible to minimize degradation of the sample. Packaging a wet swab into a plastic tube with holes or a pipet tip will considerably slow the drying process. Samples placed into devices such as these frequently take more than 24 hours to dry. A drying process that extends over many hours may jeopardize a marginal or small sample. Saliva samples placed onto swabs and then into swab containers with small holes show more degradation and yield less DNA than saliva samples placed on swabs and then into paper envelopes. Ideally, samples should be left open to the atmosphere and allowed to air dry before they are packaged in paper envelopes. In all but very humid climates, they should be dry enough to package into paper envelopes in two hours. The use of desiccants should be considered in humid environments. The following graph illustrates drying rates of 50ul bloodstains using a variety of different techniques.

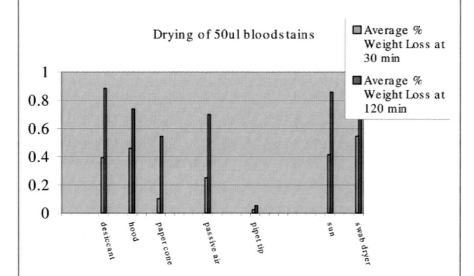

One last consideration is collecting a sample with a minimum amount of surrounding material. This should be done to minimize the contact of the biological sample with potentially deleterious material. For example, it has been found that cigarette ashes tend to inhibit the PCR reaction resulting in a failed DNA test. Therefore, when collecting cigarette butt(s) from ashtrays, it is a good idea to only

Article 13.1 Sample Handling Considerations for Biological Evidence and DNA Extracts (cont.)

collect the cigarette butt and not the accompanying ashes. This also applies to collecting biological samples from soil. To the extent that it is possible to separate the sample from the soil matrix, there will be a greater chance of a successful DNA test.

Packaging Materials:

After the sample has been collected, it should be placed into paper packaging that will protect the item against loss and contamination. This packaging can also be used to record the chain of custody and to describe the evidence item. The most important feature about this aspect of evidence packaging is that paper is a porous material and will allow air exchange with the atmosphere. This property will allow samples the chance to completely dry, even when they are not entirely dry at the time of initial packaging. *Paper envelopes or bags are the easiest way to accomplish this goal.* If the evidence is a heavily bloodstained garment, it should be allowed to dry. A piece of clean paper can then be placed over the top of the item and the item can be folded so that the paper helps to prevent direct contact between separate stains. Depending upon the stained item, more than one sheet of paper may be required. Ideally, each evidence item should be packaged in a separate, paper container. Choose a paper container large enough to easily accommodate the evidence item so that it is not necessary to "stuff" the object in the package. As long as paper bags and envelopes are not reused, they will not be a source of contamination. Once the item is ready for storage, it needs to be sealed according to agency policy.

Sample Handling Considerations in the Laboratory

Before Analysis

If it was not possible to completely air-dry samples in the field, they can be dried upon return to the laboratory. Make sure evidence is clearly labeled before it is placed into a laboratory hood or swab dryer to finish the drying process. If the item is large, try to dry one evidence item at a time in the hood. The dried evidence can then be returned to paper envelopes or bags. The next decision that will likely

Article 13.1 Sample Handling Considerations for Biological Evidence and DNA Extracts (cont.)

need to be made is: How should the evidence be stored until it is analyzed? Some types of evidence may require that the biological sample be removed from the surrounding material before storage. This would be done to minimize contact of the biological sample with potentially harmful material. For example, leather substrates may contain compounds that tend to destroy biological samples and inhibit PCR reactions. For this reason, it may be wise to remove a bloodstain from leather by swabbing the stain as soon as possible rather than cutting out the stain for analysis. Certain plant materials and soil are examples of other materials that might need to be separated from biological samples as soon as possible.

The next issue that needs to be addressed is: Where will the evidence be placed until it can be analyzed? This type of storage can usually be regarded as "short-term" storage. Three possibilities exist: (1) room temperature, (2) refrigeration or (3) frozen. If the evidence is on a smooth, non-porous material (e.g., plastic/glass/metal) or requires fingerprint processing, it should be stored at room temperature. Room temperature storage avoids the problem of condensation that is typically seen with large temperature changes that occur when the evidence item is removed from the freezer.

In general, DNA in biological samples is very stable and can tolerate room temperature storage conditions very well. However, over an extended period of time, frozen storage is generally considered to be the optimum storage condition for biological samples. This means that evidence, such as bloodstained clothing, should be held frozen. Liquid blood samples, stored in glass or plastic containers, should be held in the refrigerator since these samples can break in the freezer. Liquid blood samples containing preservatives (e.g., EDTA) are stable for a very long period of time in the refrigerator.

Article 13.1 Sample Handling Considerations for Biological Evidence and DNA Extracts (cont.)

<u>During Analysis</u>

Once analysis begins, an analyst needs to decide where to sample and how much sample to take. Evidence stains are not always uniform and it may be necessary to sample in more than one area to obtain all relevant information. Since each stain is unique, it is always a judgment call on how much sample to consume in order to optimize the chance of getting a clear result. Another simultaneous consideration is attempting to leave a sufficient amount of sample so that a second test can be conducted by the defense. If there is not enough sample to achieve both goals, it may be necessary to consult with the local district attorney's office on how to proceed.

After a sample is selected and placed into a tube for analysis, it is important that consideration be given to maintaining the quality and quantity of the evidence. Once water is added back to a sample, bacteria can begin to degrade DNA. Thus, if it is necessary to soak a sample in phosphate buffer saline to remove the cellular material, this step should be done in the refrigerator to minimize degradation by any bacteria. Certain buffers (e.g., those containing EDTA) are designed to inhibit the activity of nucleases that can breakdown DNA and these can preserve DNA in liquid form better than other liquid extractants. Another variable to keep in mind is that the efficiency of DNA extraction techniques, or how much DNA is obtained, vary with the method and the analyst. It is important to spend time to optimize each extraction method so that reasonable yields of DNA can be routinely obtained.

With respect to issues of contamination, the most at-risk samples are small stains. These samples may consist of old and degraded samples or very small volume stains. With these stains, it may be advisable to take special precautions to insure the integrity of these samples. Contamination can be minimized by preventing contact of evidence samples with any other form of biological sample. Sample tubes and reagents should be autoclaved before use. Any implement or glove that contacts the sample should be clean. It may also be important not to talk over evidence samples. Finally, when working with marginal samples it may be advisable to work in a biosafety hood.

Article 13.1 Sample Handling Considerations for Biological Evidence and DNA Extracts (cont.)

<u>After Analysis</u>

Frequently, DNA extracts or amplified products are generated during the analysis of evidence. The labeling information on these samples should be traceable to the original evidence item. This can be accomplished by assigning "sub" item numbers that correspond to the original evidence item but also reflect the exact stain.

It may not always be possible to preserve all of the extracted DNA remaining after a sample has been typed. Extracted DNA can be lost from tubes held frozen. Some of this DNA may bind to the sides of the storage tubes or be destroyed by nucleases. Recommendations that help preserve extracted DNA include using an appropriate TE buffer to store extracted DNA and keeping the extracted DNA as concentrated as possible. Dilute DNA solutions (e.g., 0 .1ng/ul), even made in the appropriate TE buffer, do not appear to be very stable over time. Finally, consider using storage tubes that seal well so that samples do not dry to a residue in the freezer.

If at all possible, keep biological evidence in the freezer for long-term storage. Although it has been possible to successfully analyze biological evidence that has been stored at room temperature for more than 25 years, the resulting STR profiles show degradation effects. In addition, relatively small amounts of DNA are usually obtained from samples held for long periods of time at room temperature indicating that DNA loss has occurred over time. Although freezing biological samples does not prevent all DNA loss or degradation, it slows DNA degradation down much more than room temperature storage. There is some anecdotal information to indicate that dry biological samples might benefit from being stored in sealed plastic bags in the freezer. The final reason to consider frozen storage is that small or marginal samples that are maintained at room temperature could degrade so that little or no typing information can be obtained.

SUMMARY OF RECOMMENDATIONS FOR THE COLLECTION OF BIOLOGICAL EVIDENCE FOR DNA ANALYSIS

Goals of Biological Evidence Collection

1. Collect as much sample as possible from a single source.

   Keep biological evidence stain concentrated/do not spread a small stain over a large substrate.

2. Insure that the sample is not inadvertently mixed with other biological samples.

   Wear gloves. Make sure that nothing contacts the evidence samples which contains another biological sample. Do not talk over biological evidence.

3. Handle the sample in a manner, which minimizes deterioration of the sample.

   Air-dry the sample as fast as possible.

Recommended Methods for Collection of Biological Evidence

Listed in Order of Desirability

1. When feasible, take object with stain. Do *not* remove stain. If stain can be easily dislodged (e.g., stain is on non-porous surface), protect it from contact with another object. One way this can be done is by immobilizing the evidence item in a cardboard container.

2. If evidence stains are found on objects that can be cut (e.g., a rug), the evidence stain can be removed by cutting it out with a pair of clean scissors. Remember to also take an "unstained" control cutting (e.g., the substrate without the stain) from the object.

3. If object cannot be moved, use a slightly dampened substrate (cotton swab or piece of plain, cotton cloth or gauze) to collect stain. Remember to collect an unstained control by swabbing an unstained area of the evidence object as very few stains can be safely collected by scraping them.
   - The size of the stain should influence the size of a substrate used to collect the stain. Thus, use a small part of a swab or a small piece of cotton cloth or piece of gauze to collect a small stain. Do not smear a small stain over a large surface.

Article 13.1 Sample Handling Considerations for Biological Evidence and DNA Extracts (cont.)

- Use a minimum amount of distilled water to dampen the swab or cloth/gauze substrate.
- To keep the stain concentrated, collect the stain on the smallest area of the swab or cotton cloth.
- Because of the attached wooden applicator stick, cotton swabs are easiest to use (tweezers are not needed).
- Use a pair of clean tweezers to manipulate cotton cloth/gauze; do not handle stain with bare hands.
- Allow all samples to air-dry as quickly as possible. The longer an evidence stain is kept wet, the more it can deteriorate.

Other Considerations

1. To avoid contamination, do not allow the biological evidence stain to come into contact with any other biological sample.
   - Each individual stain should be collected separately. Do not collect or package two separate stains together in the same container.
   - Do not allow evidence samples to come into contact with any surface, which contains residue from another biological sample (e.g., dirty tweezers, bloodstained glove, contaminated work surface).
   - Use tweezers with smooth, easy-to-clean working surfaces.
   - Tools (e.g., tweezers or scissors) can be cleaned by thoroughly rinsing with a stream of distilled water and drying thoroughly with paper tissue. Repeat this process *twice* before using tool to manipulate another sample.
   - Do not talk or cough over biological evidence.
   - Working surfaces (that could contact other samples) should be cleaned with a freshly made 10% solution of bleach. Insure that any bleach residue is thoroughly removed by wiping it down with another clean paper towel.
2. Small biological evidence (e.g., 2-mm size bloodstain or hair) is most susceptible to contamination.
   - Put on a new pair of gloves before handling these small stains. Consider wearing a mask.
   - Work on clean surfaces. If possible, work in a biosafety hood.

Article 13.1 Sample Handling Considerations for Biological Evidence and DNA Extracts (cont.)

3. Package all biological evidence in paper bags or envelopes. Do not use plastic.
   - Allow stains to air-dry before placing in paper bag or envelope.
   - Work on one evidence item at a time.
   - Insure that paper containers used to package biological evidence are sufficiently large to allow some air circulation around evidence item.
   - "Unstained controls" must be packaged separately from the evidence stain.
   - Package different evidence items in separate paper containers.
   - A piece of clean paper can be placed over a garment with a number of bloodstains. The garment can be folded so that the paper helps to prevent contact between different stains

Storage of Biological Evidence

1. If evidence sample is at risk, it might be desirable to remove it from the evidence item before storage:
   a. A crust of blood on a smooth, non-porous item may be easily dislodged and lost
   b. A biological sample on a potentially harmful substrate like leather should be removed.

2. In general, the DNA in biological samples is relatively stable at room temperature. Short-term, some evidence should be held at room temperature:
   a. Any evidence item that requires both fingerprint processing and DNA typing should be held at room temperature conditions until analysis is completed.
   b. Biological evidence on smooth, non-porous surfaces where condensation from large temperature changes might be a problem.

3. Liquid blood samples (with preservatives) are stable in the refrigerator for extended time periods. For long-term storage, frequently bloodstains are made from these liquid samples and the stains are held frozen.

4. Over any extended period of time, biological evidence is best preserved in the freezers. Freezers that do not routinely go through a defrost cycle are preferable to freezers that are "frost-free". Clothing with biological stains should be held frozen.

> **Article 13.1 Sample Handling Considerations for Biological Evidence and DNA Extracts (cont.)**
>
> 5. DNA extracts should be kept as concentrated as possible, stored in TE buffer and held frozen in airtight tubes.
>
> **References**
>
> Kobilinsky, L. <u>Recovery and Stability of DNA in Samples of Forensic Science Significance</u>. Forensic Sci. Rev 4:67, 1992.
>
> Gialamas, D. and Stockwell, D., <u>Forensic Biology Sample Collection and Handling Techniques: A Look at Methods Utilized by California Crime Labs</u>, CAC News, Summer 1995.

SUMMARY

This chapter covers the structure of DNA, DNA testing, collection of evidence, pitfalls in collection and basic interpretation of DNA results.

DISCUSSION TOPICS

Vocabulary

- Recombinant DNA
- Cloning
- CODIS
- Frye vs. United States
- mDNA
- nDNA
- Cross-contamination
- Elimination sample

REVIEW QUESTIONS

1. Discuss the uses of mitochondrial DNA testing. Include its inheritance pattern and advantages.
2. Compare and contrast mitochondrial DNA inheritance to nuclear DNA inheritance.
3. Discuss the common pitfalls of DNA testing and how to prevent them.
4. Discuss the difference between the terms 'inclusion' and 'exclusion' of a suspect.
5. Outline the important features of PCR DNA analysis.

ADDITIONAL READING

Human Genome Project
    www.ornl.gov/sci/techresources/Human_Genome/elsi/
    forensics.shtml

Medical Genetics
    www.vivo.colostate.edu/hbooks/genetics/medgen/dnatesting/dnatest_tech.html#eg3

Forensic Fact Files
    www.nifs.com.au/FactFiles/DNA/how.asp?page=how

"Collection and Preservation of Blood Evidence at Crime Scenes"
    www.crime-scene-investigator.net/blood.html

"What Every Law Enforcement Officer Should Know About DNA Evidence"
    www.ncjrs.org/nij/DNAbro/intro.html

"Understanding DNA Evidence"
    www.ojp.usdoj.gov/nij/dna.evbro/index.html

"Profiles in DNA, Celebrating the Double Helix"
    www.promega.com/profiles/601/ProfilesInDNA_601_13.pdf

Great lecture on PowerPoint about DNA, PCR and TR's
    www.bodetech.com/services/1

DNA and cold case review
    www.ncjrs.org/txtfiles1/nij/194197.txt

Reference Guide on DNA Evidence
    www.fjc.gov/public/pdf.nsf/lookup/9.dna.pdf/$File/9.dna.pdf

ENDNOTES

1. www.promega.com/geneticidproc/ussymp8proc/36.html).

2. www.ncjrs.org/txtfiles1/nij/194197.txt

3. www.ncjrs.org/txtfiles1/nij/194197.txt

4. www.fjc.gov/public/pdf.nsf/lookup/9.dna.pdf/$File/9.dna.pdf

SUPPLEMENTAL READING

The following article is a publication of the National Institute of Justice (NIJ)

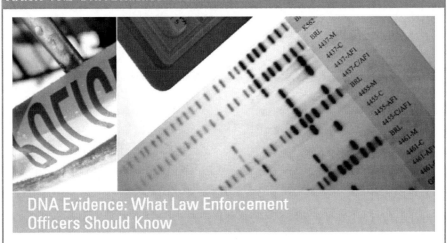

Article 13.2 DNA Evidence: What Law Enforcement Officers Should Know

DNA Evidence: What Law Enforcement Officers Should Know

Proper use of DNA (deoxyribonucleic acid) evidence at trial can help to seal a conviction or obtain an acquittal. It is therefore very important that police officers know how to manage crime scenes in order to make sure DNA evidence is collected properly. If such evidence is to be useful in court, law enforcement personnel should employ specific procedures to protect and preserve this sensitive biological material.

At the Crime Scene

Violent crime scenes often contain a wide variety of biological evidence, most of which can be subjected to DNA testing. Although not always visible to the naked eye, such evidence often is key to solving a crime, obtaining a conviction, or exonerating the falsely accused. For example, during a sexual assault, the perpetrator may leave blood, hair, saliva, semen, and skin cells on the victim's body, clothing, or carpeting or elsewhere at the scene. Scientists compare the collected biological samples against the DNA of the victim, the suspect, and any other potential suspects who may have had access to the scene. If no suspect exists, a DNA profile from the crime scene can be entered into the Combined DNA Index System (CODIS) to identify a suspect or to link serial crimes. (See "CODIS.")

Evidence Collection and Preservation

Responding officers and investigators should carry out their work at the crime scene as if it were the only opportunity to preserve and recover physical clues. Keeping DNA evidence untainted until it has been collected and recorded is the most important aspect of managing the evidence.

Proper collection is essential for successful DNA testing. Because prosecution of a case can hinge on the state of the evidence as it was collected, police investigators should take precautions, such as wearing disposable gloves and avoiding touching any other objects while handling such evidence, to avoid contamination.

Contamination also can take place if someone sneezes or coughs over the evidence or touches his or her hair, nose, or other part of the body and then touches the area containing the sample to be tested. DNA left at a crime scene also is subject to environmental contamination. Exposure to bacteria, heat, light, moisture, and mold can speed up the degradation (or erosion) of DNA. As a result, not all DNA evidence yields usable profiles. (See "Safeguard DNA Evidence and Yourself.")

Officers should not drink, eat, litter, smoke, or do anything else that might compromise the crime scene. They should remember that valuable DNA evidence may be present even though it is not visible. For example, since evidence could be on a telephone mouth or earpiece, investigators should use their own police radios instead of a telephone located at the crime scene.

To further avoid compromising evidence, any movement or relocation of potential evidence should be avoided. Officers should move evidence only if it will otherwise be lost or destroyed. In sexual assault cases, it is especially important that officers explain to victims why they should not change clothes, shower, or wash any part of their body after an assault. Depending on the nature of the assault, semen may be found on bedding or clothing, or in the anal, oral, or vaginal region. Saliva found on an area where the victim was bitten or licked

Article 13.2 DNA Evidence: What Law Enforcement Officers Should Know (cont.)

may contain valuable DNA. If the victim scratched the assailant, skin cells containing the attacker's DNA may sometimes be present under the victim's fingernails. Victims should be referred to a hospital where an exam will be conducted by a physician or sexual assault nurse examiner.

WHAT IS CODIS?

The Combined DNA Index System (CODIS) is an electronic database of DNA profiles administered through the Federal Bureau of Investigation (FBI). The system lets federal, state, and local crime labs share and compare DNA profiles. Through CODIS, investigators match DNA from crime scenes with convicted offenders and with other crime scenes using computer software, just as fingerprints are matched through automated fingerprint identification systems.

CODIS uses two indexes:
- The Convicted Offender Index, which contains profiles of convicted offenders.
- The Forensic Index, which contains DNA profiles from crime scene evidence.

The real strength of CODIS lies in solving no-suspect cases. If DNA evidence entered into CODIS matches someone in the offender index, a warrant can be obtained authorizing the collection of a sample from that offender to test for a match. If the profile match is in the forensic index, the system allows investigators—even in different jurisdictions —to exchange information about their respective cases.

Potential evidence can become contaminated when DNA from another source gets mixed with samples gathered for a specific case. In those situations, laboratory analysts have to request samples from all persons with access to the crime scene, including officers and anyone who had physical possession of the evidence while it was being recovered, processed, and examined. Maintaining a precise chain of custody of all DNA materials collected for testing is critical, as it may at some point become an issue in court. (See "Identifying

DNA Evidence.") Every action officers take at a crime scene must be fully documented.

SAFEGUARD DNA EVIDENCE AND YOURSELF

Biological material may contain hazardous pathogens, such as the hepatitis A virus, which can lead to potentially lethal diseases. At the same time, such material can easily become contaminated. To protect both the integrity of the evidence and the health and safety of law enforcement personnel, officers should:

- Wear gloves and change them often.
- Use disposable instruments or clean them thoroughly before and after handling each sample.
- Avoid touching any area where DNA might exist.
- Avoid talking, sneezing, or coughing over evidence.
- Avoid touching one's own nose, mouth, and face when collecting and packaging evidence.
- Air-dry evidence thoroughly before packaging.
- Put evidence into new paper bags or envelopes. Do not place evidence in plastic bags or use staples.

Improvements in analysis and interpretation of physical evidence recovered from crime scenes continue to develop. Properly documented and preserved DNA evidence will be given increased weight in court, so it is extremely important that an officer's approach to gathering evidence be objective, thorough, and thoughtful.

Elimination Samples

The DNA of several individuals may be present at a crime scene. So, officers must ensure that technicians collect the victim's DNA along with the DNA of anyone else who may have been present at the scene. These "elimination samples" help determine if the evidence is from a suspect or another person. The types of elimination samples to be collected depend on the details of the crime, but they are generally samples of blood or saliva.

Article 13.2 DNA Evidence: What Law Enforcement Officers Should Know (cont.)

Evidence	Possible Location of DNA on the Evidence	Source of DNA
Baseball bat or similar weapon	Handle, end	Sweat, skin, blood, tissue
Hat, bandanna or mask	Inside	Sweat, hair, dandruff
Eyeglasses	Nose or ear pieces, lens	Sweat, skin
Facial tissue, cotton swab	Surface area	Mucus, blood, sweat, semen, ear wax
Dirty laundry	Surface area	Blood, sweat, semen
Toothpick	Tips	Saliva
Used cigarette	Cigarette butt	Saliva
Stamp or envelope	Licked area	Saliva
Tape or ligature	Inside/outside surface	Skin, sweat
Bottle, can or glass	Sides, mouthpiece	Saliva, sweat
Used condom	Inside/outside surface	Semen, vaginal or rectal cells
Blanket, pillow, sheet	Surface area	Sweat, hair, semen, urine, saliva
"Through & through" bullet	Outside surface	Blood, tissue
Bite mark	Person's skin or clothing	Saliva
Fingernail, partial fingernail	Scrapings	Blood, sweat, tissue

For example, in a residential burglary where the suspect may have sipped from a glass of water, DNA samples should be obtained from every person who had access to the crime scene both before and after the burglary. The forensic technician will compare these samples with the saliva found on the glass to determine if the saliva contains probative evidence.

In homicide cases, the victim's DNA should be obtained from the medical examiner at the autopsy, even if the body is badly decomposed. This process may help to identify an unknown victim or to distinguish between the victim's DNA and other DNA found at the crime scene. (See "Thinking Solves Crimes.")

Article 13.2 DNA Evidence: What Law Enforcement Officers Should Know (cont.)

In a rape case, investigators may need to collect and analyze the DNA of every consensual sexual partner the victim had up to 4 days prior to the assault. Testing can eliminate those partners as potential sources of DNA suspected to be from the rapist. A sample should also be taken from the victim. It is important to approach the victim with extreme sensitivity and to explain fully why the request is being made. A qualified victim advocate or forensic nurse examiner can be a great help.

Evidence Transportation and Storage

When transporting and storing evidence that may contain DNA, the evidence should be kept dry and at room temperature. It should be placed in paper bags or envelopes and then sealed, labeled, and transported in a way that ensures proper identification and documents a precise chain of custody. Plastic bags should not be used because they provide a growth medium for bacteria that may degrade DNA evidence. Direct sunlight, heat, and humidity also harm DNA, so evidence should not be stored in an area that can get hot, such as a room or police car without air conditioning.

Evidence that is properly identified, preserved, and collected can be stored for years without risking extensive degradation, even at room temperature. Check with a local forensic laboratory for more information on long-term storage issues.

DNA Testing

The most common methods of DNA analysis use the polymerase chain reaction (PCR) technique. Polymerase is an enzyme involved in the natural replication, or copying, of genetic material. By helping the replication process along through a series of chemical steps, the PCR process can copy very small amounts of DNA very quickly. PCR amplification can create enough DNA to enable a laboratory analyst to generate a DNA profile, which can then be compared to other profiles. The development of the PCR technique revolutionized

Article 13.2 DNA Evidence: What Law Enforcement Officers Should Know (cont.)

the field of DNA testing by improving the success rate for analysis of old, degraded, or very small biological samples.

THINKING SOLVES CRIMES

Officers can collect DNA evidence from a wide variety of locations, and their thinking of unlikely places to look for DNA has been the catalyst for solving many cases. Examples of unusual sources of DNA evidence include the following:

- Saliva found on the flap of an envelope containing a threatening letter. The sample was analyzed and the suspect was apprehended.
- Spittle collected from the sidewalk where a suspect in a sexual assault case was under officer surveillance. Following DNA testing, the suspect was charged with the crime.
- Blood collected from a bullet that had passed through an assailant's body and lodged in the wall behind him. The assailant was identified and charged with the crime.

However, the quality or quantity of the DNA obtained from crime scene evidence may be inadequate to produce usable results, even using the PCR technique. Also, inconclusive results can occur if the sample contains a mixture of DNA from several individuals—for example, a sample taken from a victim of a gang rape. Because the PCR process copies whatever DNA is present in the sample, the contaminating DNA also is copied. Even if the suspect's DNA profile can be found in the evidence, the presence of DNA from other sources may prevent establishing either an inclusion or exclusion. In such cases, the results will likely be reported as inconclusive.

Thus, the presence of DNA from other sources may prevent the inclusion or exclusion of one individual as the source of DNA. As

Article 13.2 DNA Evidence: What Law Enforcement Officers Should Know (cont.)

with all DNA results, inconclusive findings should be interpreted in light of all the other evidence in a case.

Now and In the Future

DNA technology will continue to evolve. Some anticipated advances in its use include:

Broader implementation of the CODIS database. States will continue to enact legislation requiring DNA samples from more offenders, resulting in more crimes being solved and increased cooperation among the States. Procedures for making international matches are expected to be developed— especially with Great Britain, which has a well-developed convicted felon database.

Increased automated laboratory procedures and use of computerized analysis. Although these timesaving approaches are not expected to replace human judgments in the final review of data, automation of many of the more routine aspects of analysis is expected to result in significant cost savings.

Portable devices capable of DNA analysis. These devices, plus advances in communications technology, may permit DNA evidence to be analyzed closer to the crime scene.

Remote links to databases and other criminal justice information sources. Prompt determinations of the DNA profile at the crime scene could speed up identification of a suspect or eliminate innocent persons from being considered suspects.

Such forecasts of the future are somewhat uncertain. However, the fact that private laboratories, Federal agencies, and universities are aggressively researching these and other new technologies raises expectations that more sophisticated innovations will be developed.

Even with the latest innovations, DNA testing alone cannot provide absolute answers in every case. The prosecutor, defense counsel, judge, and law enforcement should confer on the need for such testing on a case-by-case basis.

NCJ 200908

For More Information

- Any state or local law enforcement laboratory that conducts DNA analysis should contact the FBI for CODIS software, training, and user support. Visit the CODIS Web site at http://www.fbi.gov/hq/lab/ codis/index1.htm.

- CD-ROM interactive courses on collecting and preserving DNA evidence (NCJ 182992 Beginning and NCJ 184479 Advanced) are available from the National Criminal Justice Reference Service (NCJRS) at 800–851–3420 or http://www.ncjrs.org.

- A brochure entitled What Every Law Enforcement Officer Should Know About DNA Evidence (BC 000614) is available on the NCJRS Web site at http://www.ncjrs. org/nij/DNAbro/intro.html.

- Understanding DNA Evidence: A Guide for Victim Service Providers (BC 000657) is available on the NIJ Web site at http://www.ojp.usdoj.gov/nij/dna_evbro.

ADVANCING JUSTICE THROUGH DNA TECHNOLOGY

The massive demand for DNA analyses in recent years has created a significant backlog of casework samples in crime labs across the country. These delays in processing samples pose substantial barriers to effective law enforcement and deny justice to crime victims and the public. For example, many rape kits and other evidence were thrown away in Los Angeles because investigators believed that the statutes of limitations had passed. NIJ research estimates that the number of rape and homicide cases awaiting DNA testing is approximately 350,000.

On March 11, 2003, Attorney General John Ashcroft announced a 5-year, $1 billion plan to eliminate the backlog of DNA evidence in crime labs.

(See http://www.ojp.usdoj.gov/nij/dnainitiative/welcome.html.)

If approved by Congress, the program would "not only speed the prosecution of the guilty, but also protect the innocent from wrongful prosecution," the Attorney General said.

A number of factors contribute to the inability of labs to accept and process casework samples in a timely fashion. For one thing, most State and local crime labs lack sufficient numbers of trained forensic scientists and do not have the money to hire more. Even where funds are available, there is an insufficient pool of qualified forensic scientists to hire. In addition, many State and local crime labs lack the resources and lab space necessary to obtain and use state-of-the-art automated equipment and software that would speed up DNA analyses.

Aside from the backlog of DNA evidence collected through case investigations, there is also a backlog of DNA data from known offenders waiting to be input into searchable databases. Because DNA casework analysis often requires comparisons with offender DNA profiles, the effectiveness of any DNA casework reduction strategy will depend upon up-to-date offender databases. Furthermore, while many States have statutes authorizing the collection of DNA evidence from a variety of convicted offenders, substantial numbers of authorized samples have yet to even be collected, let alone analyzed.

In its report to the Attorney General, NIJ made six recommendations to address these and other backlog issues:

1. Improve the DNA analysis capacity of public crime laboratories.

2. Provide financial assistance to State and local crime labs to help eliminate casework backlogs.

3. Develop funding to eliminate convicted offender database backlogs, and encourage aggressive programs to collect owed samples from convicted offenders.

4. Support training and education for forensic scientists, to increase the pool of available DNA analysts.

5. Provide training and education on the proper collection, preservation, and use of forensic DNA evidence to police officers, prosecutors, defense attorneys, judges, victim service providers, medical personnel, and other criminal justice personnel.

6. Support the development of improved DNA technologies, set up demonstration projects to encourage the increased use of DNA testing, and create a national forensic science commission to help ensure that the latest DNA and other forensic technologies are used to the maximum extent by criminal justice systems.

For more information, visit NIJ's DNA backlog Web page at

http://www.ojp.usdoj.gov/nij/dnabacklog. Get a free copy of Report to the Attorney General on

Delays in Forensic DNA Analysis, Washington, DC: U.S. Department of Justice, National Institute of

Justice, March 2003 (NCJ 199425), available online at

http://www.ojp.usdoj.gov/nij/pubs-sum/199425.htm or from NCJRS at 1–800–851–3420.

Chapter 14

Biological Evidence Case Studies

OVERVIEW

This chapter contains nine case studies that are directly applicable to the material in the other chapters of this book. You may or may not be familiar with them. Keeping an open mind, review each of the cases and the accompanying scientific evidence. Discussions will include how the evidence influenced the outcome of the cases and what could have been done differently during the evidence procurement to change the outcome.

CASE STUDIES

1. OJ Simpson [DNA, trace evidence chain of custody)

2. Jon Benet Ramsey [autopsy, DNA]

3. Derrick Todd Lee [DNA; sexual assault]

4. David Conahan [trace evidence]

5 Mary Bell [autopsy; interviews]

6. Kirk Bloodsworth [sexual assault, DNA]

7. Rolando Cruz & Alejandro Hernandez [sexual assault, DNA]

8. Frederick Daye [DNA]

9. Edward Honaker [sexual assault, DNA]

THE O.J. SIMPSON CASE

Background

On June 12, 1994 at about 10:15 p.m., a neighbor in the area of the 800 block of S. Bundy, in the Brentwood area of Los Angeles, reported hearing a dog barking continuously from the house. At about, 11:00 p.m. another neighbor was walking his dog and saw a white Akita with blood on its paws and the fur underneath its belly. The dog led another neighbor back to 875 S. Bundy.

At 12:13 a.m., Los Angeles Police Department patrol officers arrived. These officers walked to the entrance of 875 S. Bundy and discovered two mutilated bodies, lying on the ground in pools of blood. One of the bodies was that of a female, laying face down with her left cheek on the ground. There were apparent slash wounds to her throat and upper body. The other body was that of a male laying crouched on his right side. There were also apparent slash wounds to his throat and stab wounds on his body. Both were apparently dead. Paramedics from the Los Angeles Fire Department confirmed this at 12:45 a.m. The bodies were identified as Nicole Brown Simpson, the resident of 875 S. Bundy, and Ronald Lyle Goldman. Officers entered the house and found Simpson's children inside sound asleep.

Outside of the house, near the bodies, officers located a set of keys, a dark blue knit cap, a pager, a blood spattered white envelope and a blood stained left handed leather glove. The glove was found under a bush next to Nicole Simpson's body. There was a trail of bloody footprints leading away from the bodies to the back of the property. Alongside these footprints were drops of blood trailing in the same direction.

After establishing the identity of Nicole Simpson, Los Angeles Police detectives went to her ex-husband, Orenthal James Simpson's residence at 360 Rockingham Avenue in Los Angeles to notify him of his ex-wife's death and to arrange for him to care for their children. There was a 1994, white Ford Bronco parked on Rockingham in front of the house. The cars registration showed it belonged to "Hertz" rent-a-car. There were items inside the car that were clearly marked "Orenthal Products." Detectives noticed that there was an apparent blood spot on the door panel of the car.

The detectives were unable to reach anyone inside the house by phone. They went through the gate and contacted Simpson's daughter,

Arnelle Simpson and Simpson's friend Kato Kaelin, in separate bungalows on the property behind the main house. Arnelle Simpson assisted detectives in locating her father, who was currently in Chicago. O.J. Simpson spoke with the detectives by phone.

While at the house on Rockingham, detectives found another bloodstained glove behind the bungalows. This was a left-handed glove and an apparent match to the one found at 875 S. Bundy. After taking closer look at the Ford Bronco, detectives saw blood drops on the driver's door and the console near the passenger side. Detectives followed a trail of blood drops from the Bronco, through the west gate of the property, leading to the front door. A search warrant was later obtained for this residence and additional blood drops were found in the foyer and master bedroom.

Hair Evidence:

- Hairs consistent with that of Simpson found on cap at Bundy residence.
- Hairs consistent with that of Simpson found on Ron Goldman's shirt.

Fiber Evidence:

- Cotton fibers consistent with the carpet in the Bronco found on glove at Rockingham.
- Fibers consistent with the carpet from the Bronco found on cap at Bundy residence.

Blood Evidence:

- Killer dropped blood near shoe prints at Bundy.
- Blood dropped at Bundy was of same type as Simpson's (about 0.5% of population would match).
- Simpson had fresh cuts on left hand on day after murder.
- Blood found in Bronco.
- Blood found in foyer and master bedroom of Simpson home.
- Blood found on Simpson's driveway.

Glove Evidence

- Left glove found at Bundy and right glove found at Simpson residence are Aris Light gloves, size XL.
- Nicole Brown bought pair of Aris Light XL gloves in 1990 at Bloomingdale's.
- Simpson wore Aris Light gloves from 1990 to June 1994.

Shoe Evidence:

- Shoe prints found at Bundy were from a size 12 Bruno Magli shoe.
- Bloody shoe impression on Bronco carpet is consistent with a Magli shoe.

Simpson wore size 12 shoes.

Figure 14.1 shows the list of the 45 bloodstains introduced at trial, with their DNA evidence.

(Two types of DNA tests were used, RFLP* and PCR**. RFLP tests are more precise, but require much more DNA. PCR tests are used when only small amounts of DNA are present.)

Identification Key: OJS = O.J. Simpson, NBS = Nicole Brown Simpson, RG = Ronald Goldman

Figure 14.1 List of Bloodstains Introduced at Trial with Their DNA Evidence			
LOCATION OF STAIN	**NO. OF TESTED LOCI RFLP**	**NO. OF TESTED LOCI PCR**	**NOT EXCLUDED***
ROCKINGHAM PROPERTY			
Rockingham trail (item 6)	0	2	OJS
Rockingham trail (item 7)	0	5	OJS
Rockingham foyer	5	6	OJS
Rockingham master bathroom floor	0	1	OJS
BUNDY CRIME SCENE			
Blood pool by Nicole Brown Simpson	0	1	NBS
Blood drop by Nicole Brown Simpson	0	7	OJS
Bundy walk blood drop (item 48)	0	7	OJS
Bundy walk blood drop (item 49)	0	6	OJS
Bundy walk blood drop (item 50)	0	7	OJS
Bundy walk blood drop (item 52)	5	7	OJS

LOCATION OF STAIN	NO. OF TESTED LOCI RFLP	NO. OF TESTED LOCI PCR	NOT EXCLUDED***
Shoe impression	0	5	NBS
Blood drop on Goldman boot	5	6	NBS & RG
Brown Simpson's fingernails	0	7	NBS
Back gate (item 115)	0	2	OJS
Back gate (item 116)	0	2	OJS
Back gate (item 117)	0	2	OJS
Rockingham Glove			
Inside / back of wrist	0	1	NBS & RG
Inside / back of index finger	5	2	NBS & RG
Inside / side of middle finger	5	2	NBS & RG
Inside / back of ring finger	8	2	RG
Inside / back of hand	5	2	NBS & RG
Inside / by wrist notch	0	2	OJS & RG
Outside / near wrist notch (item G-11)	0	1	OJS, NBS, & RG
Outside/ near wrist notch (item G-12)	0	1	NBS & RG
Stitching / wrist notch	0	1	OJS, NBS, & RG
Inside / back of cuff	0	1	NBS RG
Rockingham Socks			
Ankle	14	7	NBS
Near ankle (item 42-B1)	0	2	NBS
Near ankle (item 42-B2)	0	2	NBS
LOCATION OF STAIN	NO. OF TESTED LOCI RFLP	NO. OF TESTED LOCI PCR	NOT EXCLUDED***
Upper sock / opposite side	0	2	OJS
Upper sock/ same side	9	2	OJS
Upper toe	0	2	OJS

Simpson's Bronco			
Driver door interior	0	1	OJS
Instrument panel	0	1	OJS
Driver side carpet	0	1	OJS
Steering wheel	0	1	OJS & NBS
Center console (item 30)	0	2	OJS
Center console (item 31)	0	2	OJS
Driver side wall	0	1	OJS
Driver side carpet	0	1	NBS
Center console (combination of 3 below)	4	*	OJS
Center console (item 303)	*	2	OJS
Center console (item 304)	*	2	OJS
Center console (item 305)	*	2	OJS
45 Total blood stains tested			

Source: University of Missouri-Kansas City Law School. Doug Linder, Professor of Law (Seminar in Famous Trials).(c) 1995-2004. www.law.umkc.edu/faculty/projects/ftrials/ftrials.htm

THE JON BENET RAMSEY CASE

Background

On December 26, 1996, Boulder Colorado Police responded to the home of John and Patsy Ramsey. The Ramsey's reported they had found a ransom note inside their house and that their six year old daughter, Jon Benet was missing. A few hours after the police had arrived, John Ramsey and a friend decided to conduct a thorough search of the house. It was during this search; Jon Benet's body was found wrapped in a blanket in the basement. The media coverage of this murder has been intense. There have been numerous media reports implicating the Ramsey's in the death of their daughter. Many of these reports have been based more on rumor and innuendo than on the actual evidence gathered at the Ramsey house. This murder case remains unsolved. In this case study, we will look at the evidence gathered by police.

Six-year-old Jon Benet Ramsey was found lying in the middle of the basement floor below her house. She was wrapped in a blanket with duct tape covering her mouth. Her arms were placed above her head and a white cord was wrapped tightly around her neck. This same cord was wrapped loosely around both of her wrists. There was a broken handle of a paintbrush, about four and one half inches in length, wrapped in the cord to fashion a garrote.

Jon Benet was wearing a sweatshirt over a long sleeve shirt with white pajama bottoms over white panties. An autopsy found undigested remnants of pineapple in her stomach. There was evidence to support that Jon Benet had been sexually assaulted then strangled with the garrote found at the scene.

Police criminalists found a footprint in concrete dust near the wine cellar in the basement. This footprint was from a "Hi Tech" hiking boot. Police have investigated over 400 people that had access to the Ramsey house and were not able to link this boot print to any of them.

- An unidentified palm print was found on the door to the wine cellar. Each of the Ramsey's has been eliminated as a source of this palm print.
- Pubic hair was located on the blanket that Jon Benet was found wrapped in. The Ramsey's have been eliminated as a source of this hair.

- A piece of broken glass was located underneath a basement window. The sill of this window showed signs of being disturbed.
- Scuffmarks were located on the basement wall below this window. The scuffs are not able to be identified, but suggest that someone had climbed in or out of this window. There were, however, no footprints found outside the window.
- The duct tape and cord that were found on Jon Benet's body did not match anything found in the Ramsey house.

This investigation is still ongoing. There is no evidence at this point, physical or trace, to link the Ramsey's to the murder of Jon Benet. After looking at this evidence, what do you think?

(Source: crimelibrary.com/ramsey/ramseymain.htm)

THE DERRICK TODD LEE CASE

In September of 2001, police in Baton Rouge, Louisiana, began investigating a series of murders and rapes involving female victims. The series was believed to involve five separate incidents of murder. Gina Wilson Green was the first in this series. Green was single, 41-years old at the time of the murder and was employed as a nurse and office manager of Home Infusion Network. She lived at 2151 Stanford Avenue, Baton Rouge, LA. Green was found strangled in her home at 2151 Stanford Avenue, Baton Rouge, LA on September 23, 2001.

Charlotte Murry Pace, the second in the series, was a single, 22-year old, graduate student from Louisiana State University. Pace also lived in Baton Rouge at 1221 Sharlo Avenue. Pace was found stabbed in her home around 2:00 p.m. on May 31, 2002.

Pam Kinnamore was the third victim. Kinnamore was a 42-year-old wife and mother and lived at 8338 Briarwood Place, Baton Rouge, LA. Kinnamore was the owner of Comforts and Joys in Denham Springs, LA. Kinnamore and was taken from her home the night of July 12, 2002. Her body was found on July 16, 2002 at Whiskey Bay in Iberville Parish, LA; investigators discovered that her throat had been cut.

Trinesha Dene Colomb was the next victim in the series. Colomb was a single, 23-year old future recruit of the United States Marine Corps. Colomb was the only victim from outside the Baton Rouge area. Colomb was reported missing on Thursday afternoon, November 21,

2002 from her house at 203 Diamond Drive, Lafayette, LA. Her vehicle was found in St. Landry Parish, LA, on a rural road. On November 24, 2002 in Scott, LA, Colomb's body was located. Colomb died from blunt trauma to the head.

Carrie Lynn Yoder was a 26-year old graduate student at Louisiana State University and lived in Baton Rouge, LA. Yoder was kidnapped from her home in the evening hours of 6 p.m. to midnight on March 3, 2003. A fisherman later found Yoder's body at Whiskey Bay on Thursday, March 13, 2003. An autopsy was performed on Yoder's body. It was determined that Yoder died of strangulation following a severe beating and rape. Her body was located in the same area as Pam Kinnamore.

A task force was assembled involving the local county sheriff's departments, the state police and federal investigators in an effort to apprehend this serial criminal. In each of these cases, a male DNA profile was recovered from the victim's bodies and was consistent in each incident. The Louisiana State Crime Laboratory positively matched it to the male DNA profile found on victims Green, Pace, Kinamore and Colomb linking one person to the murders of all five victims.

The task force received an investigative tip from the public about Derrick Todd Lee, a thirty four year old man from Feliciana Parish LA. Lee was married and had a young son and daughter. Investigators learned that Lee had an extensive criminal history dating back to his juvenile years. In May of 2003, Lee was contacted by investigators and submitted a voluntary DNA sample. The sample from Lee generated a DNA profile that matched the profile taken from the body of Carrie Yoder. Lee was charged with all five murders based upon the scientific link established by DNA.

(Source: State of Louisiana Multi-Agency Homicide Task Force. http://brgov.vom/taskforce)

DANIEL CONAHAN JR.: THE HOG TRAIL MURDERER

The case of the "Hog Trail Murderer" began in April of 1996 in the city of Punta Gorda, Charlotte County, Florida. On April 17, 1996, two hunters were in the woods along the forested area of U.S. Route 41 in Charlotte County. The two hunters found what appeared to be a human skull in the secluded, heavily wooded area. The hunters immediately ran to their car and found two deputy sheriffs on a lunch break at a nearby shopping center. The hunters reported what they had seen to the deputies and directed them to the specific area of the woods. The deputies believed this item to be a human skull and began to search the area further. One of the deputies found some discarded carpeting. When the deputy lifted the carpeting, he found a deceased human body inside. The body was of a naked white male. The decedent's genitals had been cut off his body and there was observable trauma to the neck, waist and wrist areas. A police canine trained to detect specific human enzymes with its olfactory sense, alerted the officer to a tree near the body. A forensic specialist collected hair and fibers from this tree for analysis. The area where the body was found was frequented by Florida hog hunters, thus the media dubbed the case "The Hog Trail Murders."

Dental records and fingerprints in this case were used to identify the victim, Richard Montgomery, 21 years old at the time of the murder. Montgomery had been reported missing by family members the day before being found by the hunters. An autopsy conducted by a forensic pathologist found Montgomery to have ligature marks on his neck, chest and abdomen and abrasions on both wrists. There were criss-cross types of injuries on Montgomery's back consistent with the victim being tied to a tree. The external genitalia had been cut from the body with an element of precision, using a cutting instrument with a sharp blade. There was evidence of sexual assault to the anus. Hemorrhagic fluid was present in the lungs, consistent with asphyxiation. The pathologist ruled the cause of death to be asphyxiation due to strangulation.

After the discovery of Montgomery, police continued to search the area from more clues. During this search, another mutilated corpse was found, followed by the discovery of three additional male skeletal remains.

Detectives interviewed Montgomery's mother, Mary Ellen Montgomery West. Montgomery's mother told them her son had mentioned making a new friend named Conahan, who lived in Punta Gorda Isles. Mrs. West also recalled her son telling her that a person had offered him a sum of money to pose in nude photos, but refused to tell her who this person was.

Detectives theorized that the suspect in this case might be preying on drifters and transients along U.S. Route 41. Detectives set up a decoy operation involving an undercover investigator posing as a transient in an attempt to lure the suspect. During this operation, Daniel Conahan was identified and arrested. Conahan solicited the undercover detective to pose for nude photos that involved progressive bondage. There were search warrants served on Conahan's residence and vehicle. During the search warrant, a paint chip was collected from Conahan's 1984 Mercury Capri. This paint sample was a match to a paint chip found in pubic hair of Montgomery at the crime scene. Fibers that were collected from Montgomery's body were matched to Conahan's residence carpet, his vehicle and backpack.

All of this evidence was successfully introduced in court and assisted in the conviction of Conahan for the first-degree murder of Montgomery. During the sentencing phase of Conahan's trial he was sentenced to death in Florida's electric chair. Due to this conviction, Conahan was not charged with the other murders related to the additional bodies found by investigators after the Montgomery murder. (Source: Daniel O. Conahan Jr. vs. State of Florida, Docket Number 00-170)

THE MARY BELL CASE

In the summer of 1968, the town of Scotswood, England, became the scene of one of the most disturbing murders in history. Three-year-old Brian Howe, who normally played close to his house, was missing. Eleven year old Mary Bell and her best friend thirteen year old Norma Bell went to Howe's house and offered to assist Brian's sister Pat, in locating the child. Pat Howe was uneasy about Brian's disappearance because of a recent death of another child in the town, Martin Brown. Martin was found dead inside a condemned house. Mary and Norma led Pat through the streets of Scotswood in search of Brian. The girls eventually led Pat to a industrial area in which the town's children would frequently play amongst discarded wreckage and old cars. Mary indicated that she had seen Brian playing behind some large concrete blocks. The local police would discover Brian's body here.

Brian's body was covered with weeds and grass. The cause of death was apparent strangulation. There were a pair of discarded scissors found next to the body, puncture wounds on both thighs and clumps of hair had been cut from the head. The genitals were partially skinned and the letter "M" was carved into the chest area of the body.

The investigation narrowed in on Mary Bell, partially because of her strange behavior after the discovery. During an interview with investigators, Mary Bell implicated herself in the crime. During questioning, Mary made a statement displaying knowledge of the scissors recovered from the scene; this was not released to the public by the investigators. Norma Bell told investigators that Mary indicated to her she killed Brian and that Mary had taken her to see the body. Mary Bell was arrested and charged with the murder of Brian Howe.

Investigators began to suspect that the death of Martin Brown might have not been an accident as originally suspected. Martin Brown was found dead in a condemned house, the apparent cause was a fall from a ledge. Mary Bell and Norma Bell were the ones who discovered the body, but there was no evidence of foul play in this incident. Upon further questioning Mary Bell admitted to pushing Martin Brown off the ledge. Mary Bell was found guilty of manslaughter because of diminished responsibility in both Brian Howe and Martin Brown's deaths.

(Source: crimelibrary.com/notorious_murders/famous/bell/index_1html)

CASE STUDIES OF WRONGFUL CONVICTIONS

THE KIRK BLOODSWORTH CASE

Kirk Bloodsworth at Northwestern University School of Law in 1998. Permission is granted by the Center for Wrongful convictions to reprint with appropriate attribution.

In July of 1984, nine-year-old Dawn Hamilton was raped and murdered in Baltimore County, Maryland. Kirk Bloodsworth, a former Marine, was linked to the crime by the testimony of five eyewitnesses. These witnesses placed Bloodsworth either with the victim or near the scene of the crime at the time it was believed to have occurred. The prosecution also introduced expert testimony that a pair of Bloodsworth's shoes was linked to marks found on the victim's body. Bloodsworth was convicted of this crime and sentenced to death.

Bloodsworth appealed his case and the Maryland Court of Appeals overturned this conviction. The Court based this decision on the finding that the prosecution deliberately withheld potentially exculpatory evidence from the defense. Bloodsworth was tried again and was convicted again. This conviction resulted in sentencing to two life terms.

In1992, Bloodsworth obtained a court order that approved the testing of biological evidence preserved from the crime scene with new DNA technology. Hamilton's shorts and underwear were compared to samples of DNA from the victim and from Bloodsworth. The testing on the panties excluded Bloodsworth. The FBI confirmed these results and Bloodsworth was released from prison in December of 1994. Bloodsworth was granted a full pardon based on his innocence.

The murder of Dawn Hamilton remained unsolved until the spring of 2003. A Baltimore County forensic biologist was reviewing the case and found stains on a sheet from the scene that had not been analyzed. DNA testing was ordered and the results were entered into the national DNA database. A positive match returned. The match linked Kimberly Shay Ruffner, who at the time was serving a sentence for another rape. Ironically, Ruffner was being held in the same facility as Bloodsworth and the two were acquainted through Bloodsworth's position working in the prison library. Ruffner was charged with Dawn Hamilton's murder in September of 2003.

(Source: Northwestern University School of Law, Center for Wrongful Convictions, 2002)

THE ROLANDO CRUZ & ALEJANDRO HERNANDEZ CASE

Rolando Cruz

Credit: Loren Santow / The Illinois Death Penalty Education Project

Alejandro Hernandez

In February, 1983 10 year old Jeanine Nicarico was abducted from her home in Naperville, IL. Later she was found dead and had been raped. Investigations narrowed on two men, Rolando Cruz and Alejandro Hernandez who were boastfully talking of the death, trying to appear as heroes and in an attempting to claim a $10,000. reward. Based on statements and witnesses, Cruz and Hernandez were convicted and sentenced to death.

Shortly after the trial, a repeat sex offender, burglar and murderer, Brian Dugan, confessed to the murder of Jeanine Nicarico. He stated he was searching for a place to burglarize and discovered 10 year old Jeanine home alone. He abducted her, raped and murdered her using a tire iron. He also confessed to two rape-murders and three rapes with similarities to the Nicarico case. DNA testing of semen found in the Nicarico victim showed Dugan was among the 14.3 percent of the male Caucasian population from whom it could have come. That same testing ruled out Hernandez, but did not rule out Cruz.

Although Dugan confessed to killing Jeanine Nicarico alone and it was corroborated by overwhelming evidence, prosecutors steadfastly refused to acknowledge that they had convicted the wrong men onto death row. The Illinois Supreme Court reversed the convictions but prosecutors retried Hernandez and Cruz and won again, largely because much of the evidence proving that Dugan had committed the crime was excluded from the courtroom.

In 1990, a volunteer legal team, led by Lawrence Marshall agreed to represent Cruz and Hernandez on appeal. After four years of arduous litigation, the Illinois Supreme Court reversed their convictions in 1994 and granted him a third trial. Before this trial, newly available DNA testing excluded Hernandez and Cruz as the child's rapists and linked Dugan to the crime. But prosecutors refused to drop the case.

During the third trial, a police officer admitted that he had lied under oath in relation to testimony about Cruz's purported 'vision' confession statement. After hearing the evidence, the trial judge directed a verdict of not guilty. Prosecutors later dropped charges against Hernandez.

In the aftermath of the Cruz trial, a special grand jury indicted four sheriff's deputies and three former prosecutors for their roles in the Cruz case. Charges included perjury and obstruction of justice. Although a DuPage Count jury acquitted them of those charges, the County agreed to pay $3.5 million settlement in civil rights claims from the defendants.

(Source: The Innocence Project. www.innocenceproject.org)

THE FREDERICK DAYE CASE

Frederick Daye

On Jan. 10, 1984, in San Diego, Calif., two men attacked a young white woman as she walked to her car. She described the first assailant as a black man with long processed hair and a metallic front tooth, and said that he pushed her into the car and then let in another man through the back. The perpetrators stole her jewelry and then raped her, and eventually stole her car and left her on the street.

Fifteen days after the rape, Frederick Daye, a slight 26-year-old black man from Des Moines, Iowa, was holding an open container of alcohol in a car that was stopped for a traffic violation. The officers, who believed that Daye fit the description of the first assailant, took his picture. From a photo array of five pictures, the victim picked Daye as her attacker. Several days later, the victim and a witness identified him in a line-up. Daye was arrested along with David Pringle, the suspected second assailant.

Daye and Pringle had separate trials. At his own trial, Daye testified that he had never seen Pringle before, and witnesses said that Daye was at a birthday party at a bar at the time of the rape. Pringle pled the Fifth Amendment and refused to testify at Daye's trial. Besides the victim's identification of Daye, the prosecution offered evidence that conventional serology revealed a match between his blood type and a semen stain, and testimony from a police officer that Daye had given a false name when they picked him up. In 1984, largely based on the victim's identification, Daye was convicted of kidnapping, robbery and rape. He was sentenced to life in prison. An appeal was denied in 1986.

In 1990, Pringle, who had been convicted of the rape, sent the trial judge a statement declaring that Daye was not involved in the crime. A public defender was appointed to investigate the statement but failed to do so. Finally, attorney Carmela Simoncini took over Daye's case and after several denied appeals persuaded an appeals court to pay for DNA testing. The DNA results came back in April 1994 and showed that the semen on the victim's clothing could not have come from Daye. Still, the prosecutors and the trial court would not reopen the case.

Simoncini brought the story to KGTV in San Diego, which broadcast several reports indicating that prosecutors were ignoring DNA results, while Los Angeles prosecutors were building their case around such evidence in the ongoing O.J. Simpson trial. Finally, San Diego District Attorney Jim Aitkins ordered his own DNA tests, and the results came back excluding Daye. His sentence was vacated, and he was released from prison on Sept. 29, 1994, after serving 10 years.

The DNA results matched both Pringle and another man. (This other man is also black and has a gold metallic tooth, which is on the right; Daye has a silver tooth on the left.) The victim, however, still maintains that Daye was the rapist. Since she has refused to come forward and to testify against him, the other man has never been charged.

After his release, Daye returned to his home in Iowa. Three months later, he married Mary Bell, his high school sweetheart whom he wrote while in prison. At first, things went smoothly: Daye got a job, went to church with Mary, and they had a daughter. However, he could not keep up with these responsibilities. He lost his job, began doing drugs and womanizing. In an effort to keep their marriage together, Daye and Mary moved to North Carolina, away from his destructive environment. However, once there, Frederick spent his days hanging out with friends and doing drugs. He sometimes would take long trips and not return for months, leaving Mary and their daughter to themselves. After five years, Mary filed for a divorce.

Daye returned to Iowa and eventually married another high school sweetheart, Castine. These days, he wakes up early with nowhere to go. He begins his day drinking a quart of beer, nursing it well into the afternoon. He goes to his aunt's house and plays cards with his sister and cousins. He says he cannot work because of his emotional distress. He cries when he talks about prison.

He has not received any compensation. With the help of his lawyer, Dwight Ritter, he has appealed to the California Board of Compensation asking for $100 for every day he spent in prison.

THE EDWARD HONAKER CASE

Credit: Christopher Little

Edward Honaker

In 1984, Edward Honaker was convicted in Virginia of numerous counts of sexual assault, sodomy and rape. He was sentenced to three life sentences and thirty-four years. The victims in this case were a woman and her boyfriend who were attacked while sleeping in their car in a rural area. A man with a gun and pretending to be a police officer accosted them and forced the boyfriend to go into the surrounding woods. He then forced the woman into his truck and, after driving to a different area, repeatedly raped her. The police were able to make a sketch of the assailant with the help of the victims.

A hundred miles away, another woman was raped and later told police that her assailant resembled Honaker, who lived nearby. His alibi checked out and he was never charged with this crime. The investigating officer, however, showed Honaker's picture to the victims of the first attack. They subsequently picked Honaker's picture out of a photo lineup. The first rape victim then made an identification of Honaker in court. She and her boyfriend also identified the Honaker's truck as similar to the one the assailant drove. Additional evidence consisted of camouflage clothing found in Honaker's house that was similar to the assailant's and the testimony of a state's forensic expert who claimed that he had matched definitively the hair found on the woman's shorts to Honaker. Honaker's defense was an alibi corroborated by three others, but discounted by the prosecutor.

Honaker eventually reached Centurion Ministries, an organization that works to free the wrongfully convicted. Centurion's investigation revealed that the victim and her boyfriend had been, at times, hypnotized and that the initial description of the assailant was inconsistent with

Honaker. Additionally, Honaker had undergone a vasectomy in 1976, a fact not known to the prosecution's witnesses and hardly even brought up at trial. Centurion then began working with the Innocence Project to secure DNA testing on the biological evidence collected in Honaker's case.

The prosecution agreed to release the evidence, which included spermatozoa on the vaginal swab, though they asserted that the spermatozoa belonged to the boyfriend. The DNA testing in this case was further complicated by the victim's claim of having a secret lover who could have contributed to the evidence.

The evidence was sent to Forensics Science Associates. Initial testing, using DQ Alpha testing, revealed that spermatozoa from the victim's shorts and from the vaginal swab did not match. Honaker was excluded from both profiles and FSA requested samples from the victim and her boyfriend. The second round of testing could not exclude the boyfriend from being the depositor of the semen on the victim's shorts, but he was excluded from the vaginal swab sample. The second boyfriend was tested by the Virginia State Laboratory and could not be eliminated as the source of spermatozoa from the vaginal swab, also using DQ Alpha testing.

FSA performed another round of testing, this time using DQ Alpha and polymarker testing. This more discriminating test revealed that Honaker and both boyfriends were excluded from being contributors of some of the spermatozoa found on the vaginal swab, and based on this DNA exclusion, Honaker filed for clemency. His petition was joined by the state. Honaker was pardoned in October 1994, after ten years of incarceration. When confronted with the fact that Honaker had undergone a vasectomy, the state's forensic expert said that he would not have testified to the definitive hair match that helped convict Honaker at trial.

(Source: The Innocence Project www.innocenceporoject.org/case/display_profile,phd?id=25)

Chapter 15

Testimony and Exhibit Preparation

OVERVIEW

The courtroom provides the ultimate test of thoroughness, efficiency and accuracy of crime scene evidence collection. Each step in the investigation will be scrutinized in detail. It is important to understand the basic components of the courtroom, testimony and exhibit preparation.

OBJECTIVES

After studying this chapter, the student will be able to:
1. Understand basic courtroom testimony skills.
2. Identify the factors involved in exhibit preparation.
3. Understand courtroom terminology.

DISCOVERY INTERVIEWS

Discovery interviews are interviews where attorneys gather information to make decisions on whether to negotiate a plea bargain or take a case to trial. During a discovery interview, both sides are present, the prosecution and defense in a criminal case and the plaintiff's attorney and defense in a civil matter. There is no need for the presentations of exhibits in these interviews. Witnesses should have any reports that were completed; these reports form the basis for the interview. The witnesses are not sworn in, however the interview is recorded.

Depositions

In a deposition, witnesses are sworn in and testimony is given under the penalty of perjury. Depositions are documented by a court reporter and are sometimes video taped. A judge is not present, just the attorneys from both sides. Depositions are equally as important as courtroom testimony. The information gathered is used to make decisions about the trial. When answering questions in this setting, pause briefly prior to providing an answer. This allows the attorneys time to raise any objections and gives the witness time to organize his or her thoughts prior to responding. Exhibits are not usually needed, unless the case is very complex and exhibits are required to demonstrate the case to the attorneys. After the deposition, the court reporter will complete a transcript of the testimony. Witnesses should review this transcript and make any needed corrections before the case reaches court.

Exhibits

Exhibits serve as illustrations to explain findings in layman's terms and in a non-inflammatory representation. The vocabulary used in exhibit should be non-technical, without jargon and in plain English at about the ninth grade level. Computer generated graphics, drawings or mannequins should be used to represent findings, rather than bloody or graphic photos. Exhibits such as these are more likely to be admitted into court than graphic photos. Depending on the situation, a judge may decide that the amount of prejudice created by these types of photos may outweigh their probative value and exclude them. Exhibits may be poster drawings, styrofoam heads with knitting needles through them to depict bullet paths, a computer graphic art representation of injuries, biological evidence, or scene diagrams.

Testimony

The weight given to an individual witness's testimony depends significantly on that witness's credibility. To enhance credibility, a witness should testify with an unbiased attitude. Preparation is also important. Witnesses should bring and be familiar with any reports. It is almost a matter or certainty that the attorneys will be well versed in these documents. When asked a question, it is appropriate to pause briefly before answering. Answer only the question asked and do not elaborate unless asked to do so. Testify to only the facts. Expert witnesses may give opinions, however the witness must be recognized as an expert by the court prior to providing an opinion. An expert witness is one who has greater knowledge of the subject matter than a reasonable person does.

When testifying in court, use layman's terms if at all possible. Never talk above the jurors using a great deal of technical jargon. Whenever possible, presenting a visual concept of the analysis, conclusions or interpretations of the evidence helps the jurors to understand the evidence you are testifying about. Explain limitations, sometimes the method is not able to do everything required to answer the question being asked about the evidence. Explain any limitations the analysis has toward the evidence if asked.

THE COURTROOM

The layout of the courtroom differs from court to court, jurisdiction to jurisdiction, and state vs. federal. However, the courtroom is typically comprised of the following people:

Prosecutor/Plaintiff

A prosecutor is the government lawyer who investigates and tries criminal cases. Typically known as a district or county attorney, state's attorney or United States attorney, he is the one who prosecutes another for a crime in the name of the government. Prosecutors are public or private. The public prosecutor is an officer appointed by the government, to prosecute all offences at the state level, he is the attorney general or his deputy, a county or district attorney. At the federal level, he is the United States Attorney.

A plaintiff is the person who initiates a lawsuit. When the document that initiates a lawsuit is called a petition rather than a complaint, the initiating person is usually referred to as the petitioner rather than the plaintiff.

Defense Attorney

A defense attorney presents the facts and assertions offered by a defendant in litigation as a reason in law or fact that the plaintiff should not recover or succeed with the claim; or, evidence offered by the accused to defeat a criminal charge. A defense attorney may be appointed by the court as a "public defender" if the defendant cannot afford an attorney.

Defendant/Accused

In criminal cases, a person is accused of the crime. In civil matters, a person or an organization is being sued. The person against whom a lawsuit is filed is usually called the defendant. In some states, or in certain types of actions, the defendant is called the respondent. The term respondent is also used to designate the person responding to an appeal.

Witness

A witness is a person who comes to court and swears under oath to give truthful evidence. Another meaning of the term involves one who is called upon to be present at a transaction, such as a wedding, or the making of a will. When a person signs his name to an instrument, such as a deed, a bond, and the like, to signify that the same was executed in his presence, he is called an attesting witness.

There are two types of witnesses in a trial, factual and expert. A factual witness is one who testifies about direct knowledge and includes things they directly see, hear or smell and is not hearsay or based on opinion. An expert witness is one who has undergone extensive training or gained knowledge in an particular area. These witnesses can take data, interpret it, and render an opinion as to its meaning to the jury.

Audience

The audience is people seated in the courtroom who do not have a direct role to play in the proceedings. They may have an interest in the trial, but are not directly involved.

Court Reporter

A court reporter is a person who makes a word-for-word record of what is said in court and produces a transcript of the proceedings upon request. They are trained to take down a verbatim account of all proceedings in the courtroom (but usually not in the judge's chambers unless a party requests it). Most court reporters today use special machines that enable them to record every word. Later, they prepare typed transcripts for use by the parties and the judge on appeal. Court reporters also record and transcribe depositions. Until recently, court reporters had to manually type out the transcript from their shorthand notes. Now, however, many reporters have machines that read the recording machine tape and create a text file that can be printed out on a standard computer printer.

Bailiff

A bailiff is a law enforcement officer, usually a deputy sheriff, deputy marshal or constable, assigned to a courtroom to keep peace and assist the judge, courtroom clerks, witnesses and jury. A bailiff may also deliver the custody and administration of lands or goods for the benefit of the owner or bailor, and is liable to render an account thereof.

Interpreter

An interpreter is a person proficient in a language other than English, and certified by the court to translate the proceedings into another language.

Jurors

The word "juror" comes from the word "juro", to swear; a person who is sworn or affirmed to serve on a jury. While the selection and other details regarding jurors differs according to location, generally they are selected from citizens. They may be compelled to serve by fine, generally receive compensation for their services, and while attending court they are often privileged from arrest in civil cases.

Typical Courtroom

COURTROOM TESTIMONY AND DEPOSITIONS

Common Terms Used by the Court System

Minutes of testimony (often taken by court reporter)

These are verbatim recordings fo the courtroom or deposition conversations. They are taken by a court reporter by use of a short-hand typewriting device and are later transcribed into a plain English language document. Some conversations may occur "off the record" but must be noted verbally prior so the court reporter doesn't record it.

Subpoena

A court order requiring an individual to testify in court.

Interrogatory

Any one of a numbered list of written questions submitted in a legal proceeding to an opposing party to a lawsuit as part of discovery.

Deposition

A person gives his or her deposition when he or she, accompanied by an attorney, answers questions put by the other side's attorney regarding the facts of the case. Depositions are under oath and generally take place in an attorney's office. A court reporter is present and everything that is said is recorded.

Subpoena Duces Tecum

A subpoena duces tecum is a court order requiring a witness to bring documents or other piece of evidence in the possession or under the control of the witness to a certain place, at a certain time. This subpoena must be served personally on the person subpoenaed.

Opening statement

At the beginning of the trial, each side has the opportunity to make an opening statement explaining its case, but is not required to do so. Generally, in an opening statement, attorneys for each party will explain the claims and outline the evidence they will use to prove their party's claim.

Direct Examination

Direct examination is the questioning of a witness in a trial or other legal proceeding, conducted by the party who called the witness to testify.

Voir Dire

French (pronounced "vwar deer"), and means "to speak the truth." The process of interviewing prospective jurors or witnesses under oath to determine their competence or suitability. It includes the process by which judges and lawyers select a jury from among those eligible to serve. The prospective jurors are questioned to determine their knowledge of the facts of the case and a willingness or ability to render an impartial verdict based only on the evidence presented in court. This allows potential prejudiced jurors to be excluded by either the prosecutor or defense attorney.

Cross Examination

In a trial or legal proceeding, cross-examination is the formal questioning of a witness by the party opposed to the party that called the witness to testify.

Re-Direct Examination

Questioning a witness about matters brought up during cross-examination. They are asked by the attorney who called the witness to the stand.

Re-Cross Examination

Questioning a witness about matters brought up during re-direct examination. They are asked by the opposing attorney.

Questions by Juries

In some jurisdictions, the jurors are invited to ask their own questions of the witness after re-direct. These questions must be submitted to and approved in advance by the judge.

Juries

Juries are persons selected according to law and sworn to inquire into and declare a verdict on matters of fact. A body of people selected according to law for the purpose of deciding some controversy. This mode of trial by jury was adopted soon after the conquest of England by William and was fully established for the trial of civil suits in the reign of Henry II. In the old French law, they are called inquests or tourbes of ten men.

Juries are either grand juries or petit juries. The former having been discussed elsewhere, it will only be necessary to consider the latter. A petit jury consists of twelve citizens duly qualified to serve on juries, impaneled and sworn to try one or more issues of the facts submitted to them. These sworn citizens (jurors) are asked to give a judgment of these facts. "Verdict" is the term for this type of a judgement.

The Constitution of the United States directs that 'the trial of all crimes, except in cases of impeachment, shall be by jury;' and this invaluable institution is secured by the several state constitutions. The Constitution of the United States also provides that in suits at common law, where the value in controversy shall exceed twenty dollars, the right of trial by jury shall be preserved. [7th Amendment]

It is scarcely practical to give the rules established in the different states to secure impartial juries. However, in all states, the selection and list of persons who are asked to serve on the jury, is made by

.disinterested officers and the jurors are selected by lots or impartial groupings.

Sequestered

Sometimes juries are sequestered from outside influences during their deliberations. It means to separate.

TIPS FOR TESTIMONY

When testifying in court, use layman's terms if at all possible. Never talk above the jurors using a great deal of technical jargon. Receive the questions from the questioning attorney, but direct your attention and answers to the jury during your reply. Illustrations, graphics and tables are helpful. Whenever possible, presenting a visual concept of the analysis, conclusions or interpretations of the evidence helps the jurors to understand the evidence you are testifying about. Sometimes the method used to evaluate the evidence will not be able to answer the question being asked. If asked, explain any limitations the analysis has regarding the evidence.

When you prepare for your court experience, keep the following in mind:

Always tell the truth. At trial, as in all other matters, honesty is the best policy. If you tell the truth and tell it accurately, nobody can cross you up. Do not guess or make up an answer. If you do not know the answer, it is best to say, "I don't know." If you are asked about details that you do not remember it is best to say, "I don't remember".

- Dress neatly and conservatively, The way you dress and present yourself is a direct reflection on you. You want to be sure that your appearance and manner do not distract the judge or jury from careful consideration of your testimony. Police officers should either be in uniform or a sport coat or suit and tie (men), or comparable attire (women). No tinted glasses or flashy jewelry. Be sure your shoes are polished and your clothing is neat and well-pressed.

- Be attentive. You should remain alert at all times so that you can hear, understand and give a proper response to each question. If the judge or jury gets the impression that you are bored or indifferent, they may tend to disregard your testimony.

- Use good posture and do not slouch.

- Be courteous.

- A question should be answered, "Yes, sir," or "No, sir," and the judge should be addressed as "Your Honor."

- Take your time and speak clearly and loudly. When you are sworn in, respond clearly and confidently: "I do". Give questions some thought before responding to be sure you understand it. The juror farthest from you should be able to hear distinctly what you have to say. Do not chew gum and keep your hands away from your mouth. Since all testimony is recorded, do not nod your head "yes" or "no."

- Be serious in the courtroom. Avoid joking and wisecracks in the jury's presence. The jury is sitting in judgment of another person whose liberty is at stake. That is always a very serious matter. Beware of hallway actions and conversations. Be aware of activities such as lunch or casual conversations with an attorney or other witness as it gives an impression of bias to the opposing attorney or jury member.

- Answer all questions directly. Answer only the questions asked, and then stop. Avoid "volunteering" information. If you do not understand a question, ask that it be explained. Do not look at the prosecutor for help while you are testifying and never ask the judge if you have to answer. This will give the jury the impression that you are holding something back.

- Do not lose your temper. Some attorneys may attempt to wear you down so that you will lose your temper and say things that are not correct. Do not argue with the attorneys. They have a right to question you, and many are very expert in this craft.

- Beware of questions involving distance and time. If you make an estimate, make sure that everyone understands that you are estimating.

- Beware of questions asking if you are willing to swear to your version of the events. You were "sworn" to tell the truth when you took the stand, do not be afraid of saying so.

- Beware of questions asking if you have spoken to the prosecutor, the witnesses, or other officers. If you have, admit it freely. This preparation before trial is expected in each case. If you are asked if you talked with the prosecutor about your testimony, admit that you met with him, talked about the case and he instructed you to tell the truth.

- Beware of questions asking why you don't like the defendant. You may best respond by stating that you feel sorry for any man in trouble, but you must tell the truth, and if the defendant is guilty, he should be convicted.

- Beware of questions asking you if another witness was telling the truth or lying. You can only tell the truth based upon your observations. You have no way of knowing what another person observed, especially when you did not hear that person testify.

- Beware of the simple question, "Why are you here today?" You are not here to volunteer information in order to convict. You are not an advocate. You are an unbiased witness. You appeared at trial in response to being served with a subpoena issued by the court clerk.

- Give positive, definite answers when at all possible. Avoid saying, "I think, I believe, in my opinion." A witness testifies to facts, not beliefs or opinions.

- No comment should ever be made about polygraphs or the prior criminal record of the defendant unless specifically asked by counsel. If an objection is made while you are testifying, stop and await instructions from the judge.

- Be wary of too many yes/no responses following rapidly fired questions to you as a witness. It is a tactic used to paint you into a corner. Slow down the pace by slightly hesitating in your responses or respond with a short comment followed by "yes" or "no." Try to anticipate the direction the questioning may be going.

- Be impartial. Testimony is more believable by maintaining responses reflecting the facts. Whether they are good or bad for the case will ultimately be decided by the jury.

- Be yourself. Do not use "legalese" or police "lingo" just for the sake of impressing the jury. It will have the opposite effect. Saying that "At 2140 hours the perpetrator exited the northeast door of the motor vehicle and started flight with responding officers in pursuit, resulting in apprehension," can be much more effectively stated: "At twenty till ten, the defendant got out of his car from the passenger side and ran, but was chased and caught by other officers."

The most effective witness is one who can tell his or her story comfortably. Just tell the truth and be yourself. Everything else will take care of itself.

Objections

Objections by attorneys regarding testimony should not be taken personally. The objections are typically over a point of law, although sometimes may be over something you said. When an objection is made, the judge must rule on the objection based on the reason for the objection.

The objection may be sustained, that is, the judge agrees with the objection that the answer to the question should not be given or should be stricken from the testimonial record. If the judge sustains the objection, do not continue with your testimony.

When the objection is over ruled, the judge disagrees with the objection and you may continue to provide the answer.

The compound question is the fault of the attorney asking the question. Typically, the question asks for more than one answer because there are several questions in the one overall question similar to a compound sentence. The attorney should rephrase the question if the judge sustains the objection. Be careful answering these questions. It may reflect a compound sentence in which your response may be different for each portion. You may ask for the questions to be repeated or restated because you are unable to answer the question in that format.

A "non-responsive" objection may be made. The attorney asking the question usually makes this objection due to the witness either not answering the question or the answer was one the attorney did not like. It is appropriate for a witness to inform the attorney that the question was not understood and to ask for the question to be rephrased.

SUMMARY

The courtroom is where the details of any case are scrutinized and evaluated. Thorough testimony and exhibit preparation will facilitate a clear understanding of the facts by the jury. Preparation is the key to effective presentation of a case at trial.

DISCUSSION QUESTIONS

1. What is the purpose of discovery interviews?

2. What factors are important in testifying effectively?

3. What are the elements of a well-prepared exhibit?

ADDITIONAL READING

Supplemental information is available from the following web sites:
    www.verdictsystems.com/library/courtrooms/court2.htm
    www.oak-net.org/stories/crtpro.html
    www.stvincent.ac.uk/Resources/WMidPol/Court/courtlayout.html

Glossary

ABFO scales (American Board of Forensic Odontology). An L-shaped piece of plastic used in photography that is marked with circles, black and white bars, and 18-percent gray bars to assist in distortion compensation and provide exposure determination. For measurement, the plastic piece is marked in millimeters.

absorption. Passage of nutrients, drugs or alcohol across the wall of the stomach and small intestine into the blood stream where it is distributed throughout the body.

acetate. Soft fiber commonly used in women's apparel, household draperies, and quilted bed products.

acid phosphatase. An enzyme found in high concentration in semen and secreted by the prostate gland. Useful test in determining the presence of semen even in the absence of sperm in sexual assault cases.

Adenine (A). One of the four bases, or nucleotides, that make up the DNA molecule. Adenine only binds to thymine. See nucleotide.

affinal method. A method for computing the single locus profile probabilities for a theoretical subpopulation by adjusting the single locus profile probability, calculated with the product rule from the mixed population database, by the amount of heterogeneity across subpopulations. The model is appropriate even if there is no database available for a particular subpopulation, and the formula always gives more conservative probabilities than the product rule applied to the same database.

algor mortis. The process in which the body temperature continually cools after death until it reaches the ambient or room temperature.

allele. In classical genetics, an allele is one of several alternative forms of a gene. A biallelic gene has two variants; others have more. Alleles are inherited separately from each parent, and for a given gene, an individual may have two different alleles (heterozygosity) or the same allele (homozygosity). In DNA analysis, the term is applied to any DNA region (whether or not it constitutes a gene) used for analysis.

allele-specific oligonucleotide (ASO) probe. Oligonucleotide probes used in a PCR-associated detection technique to identify the presence or absence of certain base pair sequences identifying different alleles. The probes are visualized by an array of dots rather than by the electrophoretograms associated with RFLP analysis. Also see sequence-specific oligonucleotide (SSO) probe.

alternate light source. Equipment used to produce visible and invisible light at various wavelengths to enhance or visualize potential items of evidence (fluids, fingerprints, clothing fibers, etc.).

Alu sequences. A family of short interspersed elements (SINEs) distributed throughout the genomes of primates.

alveoli. Small air filled sacs forming the basic component of lungs and respiratory gas exchange. They contain thin walls where air and other vapors are easily exchanged with the blood so oxygen can be distributed throughout the body and carbon dioxide can be excreted.

amorphous solid. Solid in which the constituent atoms or molecules are arranged in random or disordered positions.

amplification. Increasing the number of copies of a DNA region, usually by PCR.

amplified fragment length polymorphism (AMP-FLP). A DNA identification technique that uses PCR-amplified DNA fragments of varying lengths. The DS180 locus is a VNTR whose alleles can be detected with this technique.

anagen phase of hair growth. Initial growth phase during which the hair follicle is actively producing hair and may last up to six years. The root is attached to the follicle for continued growth, giving the root bulb a flame shaped appearance.

analgesic. Drug or substance that lessens or eliminates pain. Can be something over the counter such as aspirin, tylenol or ibuprofen or a prescription medication like morphine.

antibody. A protein (immunoglobulin) molecule, produced by the immune system, that recognizes a particular foreign antigen and binds to it; if the antigen is on the surface of a cell, this binding leads to cell aggregation and subsequent destruction.

anticoagulant. Substance preventing the clotting of blood. Usually heparin or EDTA and is used in blood drawing tubes.

antigen. A molecule (typically found in the surface of a cell) whose shape triggers the production of antibodies that will bind to the antigen.

aspermia. The absence of sperm and signifying sterility in males.

autoradiograph (autoradiogram, autorad). In RFLP analysis, the x-ray film (or print) showing the positions of radioactively marked fragments (bands) of DNA, indicating how far these fragments have migrated, and hence their molecular weights.

autosome. A chromosome other than the X and Y sex chromosomes.

band. See autoradiograph.

band shift. Movement of DNA fragments in one lane of a gel at a different rate than fragments of an identical length in another lane, resulting in the same pattern "shifted" up or down relative to the comparison lane. Band-shift does not necessarily occur at the same rate in all portions of the gel.

base pair (bp). Two complementary nucleotides bonded together at the matching bases (A and T or C and G) along the double helix "backbone" of the DNA molecule. The length of a DNA fragment often is measured in numbers of base pairs (1 kilobase (kb) = 1000 bp); base pair numbers also are used to describe the location of an allele on the DNA strand.

Bayes' theorem. An elementary formula that relates certain conditional probabilities. It can be used to describe the impact of new data on the probability that a hypothesis is true.

Becke line. Bright halo that is observed near the border of a particle immersed in a liquid of a different refractive index.

bin, fixed. In VNTR profiling, a bin is a range of base pairs (DNA fragment lengths). When a database is divided into fixed bins, the proportion of bands within each bin is determined and the relevant proportions are used in estimating the profile frequency.

bins, floating. In VNTR profiling, a bin is a range of base pairs (DNA fragment lengths). In a floating bin method of estimating a profile frequency, the bin is centered on the base pair length of the allele in question, and the width of the bin can be defined by the laboratory's matching rule (e.g., ±5% of band size).

bindle paper. Clean paper folded to use to contain trace evidence, sometimes included as part of the packaging for collecting trace evidence.

binning. Grouping VNTR alleles into sets of similar sizes because the alleles' lengths are too similar to differentiate.

biohazard bag. A container for materials that have been exposed to blood or other biological fluids and have the potential to be contaminated with hepatitis, AIDS, or other viruses.

biological fluids. Fluids that have human or animal origin, most commonly encountered at crime scenes (e.g., blood, mucus, perspiration, saliva, semen, vaginal fluid, urine).

biological weapon. Biological agents used to threaten human life (e.g., anthrax, smallpox, or any infectious disease).

birefringence. Difference in the two indices of refraction exhibited by most crystalline materials. When observed under polarized light, the particles appear to be glowing with a different color.

black powder. Type of gunpowder composed of a mixture of potassium nitrate, carbon and sulfur. Was the first type of gunpowder used in muzzle loaders and bullets. Leaves abundant soot.

blind proficiency test. See proficiency test.

bloodborne pathogen. Infectious, disease-causing microorganisms that may be found or transported in biological fluids.

boundaries. The perimeter or border surrounding potential physical evidence related to the crime.

capillary electrophoresis. A method for separating DNA fragments (including STRs) according to their lengths. A long, narrow tube is filled with an entangled polymer or comparable sieving medium, and an electric field is applied to pull DNA fragments placed at one end of the tube through the medium. The procedure is faster and uses smaller samples than gel electrophoresis, and it can be automated.

case file. The collection of documents comprising information concerning a particular investigation. (This collection may be kept in case jackets, file folders, ring binders, boxes, file drawers, file cabinets, or rooms. Sub-files are often used within case files to segregate and group interviews, media coverage, laboratory requests and reports, evidence documentation, photographs, videotapes, audiotapes, and other documents.)

case identifiers. The alphabetic and/or numeric characters assigned to identify a particular case.

catagen phase of hair growth. A transition stage between the anagen and telogen phases of hair growth during which the hair continues to grow, but at a decreasing rate; can last anywhere from two to three weeks.

catalyst. Substance that accelerates a chemical reaction in a solution but remains unaltered by the reaction. Some chemical reactions proceed very slowly or not at all without the presence of the catalyst.

ceiling principle. A procedure for setting a minimum DNA profile frequency proposed in 1992 by a committee of the National Academy of Science. One hundred persons from each of 15—20 genetically homogeneous populations spanning the range of racial groups in the United States are sampled. For each allele, the higher frequency among the groups sampled (or 5%, whichever is larger) is used in calculating the profile frequency. Compare interim ceiling principle.

Celsius scale. The temperature scale using the melting point of ice as 0 degrees and the boiling point of water as 100 degrees, with 100 equal divisions or degrees between. The formula for conversion between Celsius and Fahrenheit is: F temp $= 1.80 \times$ (C Temp) $+ 32$.

chain of custody. A process used to maintain and document the chronological history of the evidence. (Documents should include name or initials of the individual collecting the evidence, each person or entity subsequently having custody of it, dates the items were collected or transferred, agency and case number, victim's or suspect's name, and a brief description of the item.)

chemical enhancement. The use of chemicals that react with specific types of evidence (e.g., blood, semen, lead, fingerprints) in order to aid in the detection and/or documentation of evidence that may be difficult to see.

chemical threat. Compounds that may pose bodily harm if touched, ingested, inhaled, or ignited. These compounds may be encountered at a clandestine laboratory, or through a homemade bomb or tankard leakage (e.g., ether, alcohol, nitroglycerin, ammonium sulfate, red phosphorus, cleaning supplies, gasoline, or unlabeled chemicals).

chip. A miniaturized system for genetic analysis. One such chip mimics capillary electrophoresis and related manipulations. DNA fragments, pulled by small voltages, move through tiny channels etched into a small block of glass, silicon, quartz, or plastic. This system should be useful in analyzing STRs. Another technique mimics reverse dot blots by placing a large array of oligo-nucleotide probes on a solid surface. Such hybridization arrays should be useful in identifying SNPs and in sequencing mitochondrial DNA.

chromatography. Any of several analytical techniques whereby organic mixtures are separated into their components by their attraction to a stationary phase while being propelled by a moving phase.

chromosome. A rod-like structure composed of DNA, RNA, and proteins. Most normal human cells contain 46 chromosomes, 22 autosomes and a sex chromosome (X) inherited from the mother, and another 22 autosomes and one sex chromosome (either X or Y) inherited from the father. The genes are located along the chromosomes. See also homologous chromosomes.

clean/sanitize. The process of removing biological and/or chemical contaminants from tools and/or equipment (e.g., using a mixture of 10-percent household bleach and water).

coding DNA. A small fraction of the human genome contains the "instructions" for assembling physiologically important proteins. The remainder of the DNA is "non-coding."

CODIS (combined DNA index system). A collection of databases on STR and other loci of convicted felons maintained by the FBI.

collect/collection. The process of detecting, documenting, or retaining physical evidence.

comparison samples. A generic term used to describe physical material/evidence discovered at crime scenes that may be compared with samples from persons, tools, and physical locations. Comparison samples may be from either an unknown/questioned or a known source. *Samples whose source is unknown/questioned are of three basic types*: **1.** Recovered crime scene samples whose source is in question (e.g., evidence left by suspects, victims). **2.** Questioned evidence that may have been transferred to an offender during the commission of the crime and taken away by him or her. Such questioned evidence can be compared with evidence of a known source and can thereby be associated/linked to a person/vehicle/tool of a crime. **3.** Evidence of an unknown/questioned source recovered from several crime scenes may also be used to associate multiple offenses that were committed by the same person and/or with the same tool or weapon. *Samples whose source is known are of three basic types*: **1.** A standard/reference sample is material of a verifiable or documented source which, when compared with evidence of an unknown source, shows an association or linkage between an offender, crime scene, and/or victim (e.g., a carpet cutting taken from a location suspected as the point of transfer for comparison with the fibers recovered from the suspect's shoes, a sample of paint removed from a suspect vehicle to be compared with paint found on a victim's vehicle following an accident, or a sample of the suspect's and/or victim's blood submitted for comparison with a bloodstained shirt recovered as evidence). **2.** A control/blank sample is material of a known source that presumably was uncontaminated during the commission of the crime (e.g., a sample to be used in laboratory testing to ensure that the surface on which the sample is deposited does not interfere with testing. For example, when a bloodstain is collected from a carpet, a segment of unstained carpet must be collected for use as a blank or elimination sample). **3.** An elimination sample is one of known source taken from a person who had lawful access to the scene (e.g., fingerprints from occupants, tire tread impressions from police vehicles, footwear impressions from emergency medical personnel) to be used for comparison with evidence of the same type.

complementary sequence. The sequence of nucleotides on one strand of DNA that corresponds to the sequence on the other strand. For example, if one sequence is CTGAA, the complementary bases are GACTT.

compound. A pure substance composed of two or more elements.

contamination. The unwanted transfer of material from another source to a piece of physical evidence.

control/blank sample. See comparison samples.

cortex of a hair. The main body of the hair shaft and contained within the protective layer of the cuticle.

cross-contamination. The unwanted transfer of material between two or more sources of physical evidence.

crystalline solid. Solid in which the constituent atoms have a regular arrangement.

curare. Extract of the "Strychnos Toxitera" vine used in medicine to induce muscle paralysis including muscles used in respiration.

cytosine (C). One of the four bases, or nucleotides, that make up the DNA double helix. Cytosine only binds to guanine. See nucleotide.

D-loop. A portion of the mitochrondrial genome known as the "control region" or "displacement loop" instrumental in the regulation and initiation of mtDNA gene products.

database. A collection of DNA profiles.

degradation. The breaking down of DNA by chemical or physical means.

denature, denaturation. The process of splitting, as by heating, two complementary strands of the DNA double helix into single strands in preparation for hybridization with biological probes.

deoxyribonucleic acid (DNA). The molecule that contains genetic information. DNA is composed of nucleotide building blocks, each containing a base (A, C, G, or T), a phosphate, and a sugar. These nucleotides are linked together in a double helix—two strands of DNA molecules paired up at complementary bases (A with T, C with G). See adenine, cytosine, guanine, thym-ine.

depressant. Substance used to depress the functions of the central nervous system; they also calm irritability and anxiety and may induce sleep.

diploid number. See haploid number.

DNA polymerase. The enzyme that catalyzes the synthesis of double-stranded DNA.

DNA probe. See probe

DNA profile. The alleles at each locus. For example, a VNTR profile is the pattern of band lengths on an autorad. A multilocus profile represents the combined results of multiple probes. See genotype.

DNA sequence. The ordered list of base pairs in a duplex DNA molecule or of bases in a single strand.

documentation. Written notes, audio/videotapes, printed forms, sketches and/or photographs that form a detailed record of the scene, evidence recovered, and actions taken during the search of the crime scene.

DQA. The gene that codes for a particular class of Human Leukocyte Antigen (HLA). This gene has been sequenced completely and can be used for forensic typing. See human leukocyte antigen.

DQ. The antigen that is the product of the DQA gene. See DQA, human leukocyte antigen.

dying declaration. Statements made by a person who believes he or she is about to die, concerning the cause or circumstance surrounding his or her impending death.

EDTA. A preservative added to blood samples.

electromagnetic spectrum. The entire range of radiation energy from the most energetic cosmic rays to the least energetic radio waves.

electrophoresis. See capillary electrophoresis, gel electrophoresis.

electron. A negatively charges particle that is one of the fundamental structural units of the atom.

electrophoresis. An analytical technique where there is separation of molecules through their migration on a support medium while under the influence of an electrical current.

element. A fundamental particle of matter. An element cannot be broken down into simpler substances by chemical means. (There are 89 natural elements.)

elimination sample. See comparison samples.

emission spectrum. Light emitted from a source and separated into its component colors or frequencies.

endonuclease. An enzyme that cleaves the phosphodiester bond within a nucle-otide chain.

environmental insult. Exposure of DNA to external agents such as heat, moisture, and ultraviolet radiation, or chemical or bacterial agents. Such exposure can interfere with the enzymes used in the testing process, or otherwise make DNA difficult to analyze.

enzyme. A protein that catalyzes (speeds up or slows down) a reaction.

enzymes. Type of protein that acts as a catalyst for certain specific reactions.

ethidium bromide. A molecule that can intercalate into DNA double helices when the helix is under torsional stress. Used to identify the presence of DNA in a sample by its fluorescence under ultraviolet light.

evidence identifiers. Tape, labels, containers, and string tags used to identify the evidence, the person collecting the evidence, the date the evidence was gathered, basic criminal offense information, and a brief description of the pertinent evidence.

Fahrenheit scale. The temperature scale using the melting point of ice as 32 degrees and the boiling point of water as 212 degrees, with 180 equal divisions or degrees between. The conversion scale between Celsius and Fahrenheit scales is: F Temp = 1.80 x (C Temp) + 32

fallacy of the transposed conditional. See transposition fallacy.

false match. Two samples of DNA that have different profiles could be declared to match if, instead of measuring the distinct DNA in each sample, there is an error in handling or preparing samples such that the DNA from a single sample is analyzed twice. The resulting match, which does not reflect the true profiles of the DNA from each sample, is a false match. Some people use "false match" more broadly, to include cases in which the true profiles of each sample are the same, but the samples come from different individuals. Compare true match. See also match, random match.

first responder(s). The initial responding law enforcement officer(s) and/or other public safety official(s) or service provider(s) arriving at the scene prior to the arrival of the investigator(s) in charge.

fluorescence. To emit visible light when exposed to light of a shorter wavelength. (ultraviolet light)

gas (vapor). A state of matter in which the attractive forces between molecules are small enough to permit them to move with complete freedom.

gas chromatography. An analytical method to Separate mixtures on the basis of their distribution between a stationary liquid phase and a moving gas phase. A plot of the recorder responses (vertical axis) verses time (horizontal axis).

gel, agarose. A semisolid medium used to separate molecules by electrophoresis.

gel electrophoresis. In RFLP analysis, the process of sorting DNA fragments by size by applying an electric current to a gel. The different-sized fragments move at different rates through the gel.

gene. A set of nucleotide base pairs on a chromosome that contains the "instructions" for controlling some cellular function such as making an enzyme. The gene is the fundamental unit of heredity; each simple gene "codes" for a specific biological characteristic.

gene frequency. The relative frequency (proportion) of an allele in a population.

genetic drift. Random fluctuation allele frequencies from generation to generation.

genetics. The study of the patterns, processes, and mechanisms of inheritance of biological characteristics.

genome. The complete genetic makeup of an organism, comprising roughly 100,000 genes in humans.

genotype. The particular forms (alleles) of a set of genes possessed by an organism (as distinguished from phenotype, which refers to how the genotype expresses itself, as in physical appearance). In DNA analysis, the term is applied to the variations within all DNA regions (whether or not they constitute genes) that are analyzed.

genotype, single locus. The alleles that an organism possesses at a particular site in its genome.

genotype, multilocus. The alleles that an organism possesses at several sites in its genome.

guanine (G). One of the four bases, or nucleotides, that make up the DNA double helix. Guanine only binds to cytosine. See nucleotide.

Hae III. A particular restriction enzyme.

hallucinogen. Substance that induces changes in mood, attitude, thought, or perception. They can be auditory, visual or perceptual disturbances.

haploid number. Human sex cells (egg and sperm) contain 23 chromosomes each. This is the haploid number. When a sperm cell fertilizes an egg cell, the number of chromosomes doubles to 46. This is the diploid number.

haplotype. A specific combination of linked alleles at several loci.

Hardy-Weinberg equilibrium. A condition in which the allele frequencies within a large, random, intrabreeding population are unrelated to patterns of mating. In this condition, the occurrence of alleles from each parent will be independent and have a joint frequency estimated by the product rule. See independence, linkage disequilibrium.

heavy metal. Category of poisons that include: arsenic, bismuth, antimony mercury, and thallium.

heteroplasty. The condition in which some copies of mitochondrial DNA in the same individual have different base pairs at certain points.

heterozygous. Having a different allele at a given locus on each of a pair of homologous chromosomes. See allele. Compare homozygous.

homologous chromosomes. The 44 autosomes (non-sex chromosomes) in the normal human genome are in homologous pairs (one from each parent) that share an identical set of genes, but may have different alleles at the same loci.

human genome. The total DNA content found within the nucleus of a cell. In humans, it is composed of approximately 3 billion base pairs of genetic information.

human leukocyte antigen (HLA). Antigen (foreign body that stimulates an immune system response) located on the surface of most cells (excluding red blood cells and sperm cells). HLAs differ among individuals and are associated closely with transplant rejection. See DQA.

homozygous. Having the same allele at a given locus on each of a pair of homologous chromosomes. See allele. Compare heterozygous.

hybridization. Pairing up of complementary strands of DNA from different sources at the matching base pair sites. For example, a primer with the sequence AGGTCT would bond with the complementary sequence TCCAGA on a DNA fragment.

impression evidence. Objects or materials that have retained the characteristics of other objects that have been physically pressed against them.

independence. Two events are said to be independent if one is neither more nor less likely to occur when the other does.

initial responding officer(s). The first law enforcement officer(s) to arrive at the scene.

inorganic. A chemical compound not based on carbon.

interim ceiling principle. A procedure proposed in 1992 by a committee of the National Academy of Sciences for setting a minimum DNA profile frequency. For each allele, the highest frequency (adjusted upward for sampling error) found in any major racial group (or 10%, whichever is higher), is used in product-rule calculations. Compare ceiling principle.

investigator(s) in charge. The official(s) responsible for the crime scene investigation, and is sometime called the "case agent."

keratin. Hardened cells creating a tough outer shell surrounding a cuticle of a hair or surface of the skin.

kilobase (kb). One thousand bases.

known. See comparison samples.

laminated glass. Two sheets of ordinary glass bonded together with a plastic film. Common source is windshields of vehicles where the plastic serves to provide cohesion to areas where it fractures and prevent injuries.

latent print. A print impression not readily visible, made by contact of the hands or feet with a surface resulting in the transfer of materials from the skin to that surface.

linkage. The inheritance together of two or more genes on the same chromosome.

linkage equilibrium. A condition in which the occurrence of alleles at different loci is independent.

litigation. To carry out a legal contest by judicial process; can be either civil or criminal proceedings.

locus. A location in the genome, i.e., a position on a chromosome where a gene or other structure begins.

man-made fibers. Fibers derived from either natural or synthetic polymers; the fibers are typically made by forcing the polymeric material through the holes of a spinneret.

mass spectroscopy. The separation of elements or molecules according to their molecular weight. In the version being developed for DNA analysis, small quantities of PCR-amplified fragments are irradiated with a laser to form gaseous ions that traverse a fixed distance. Heavier ions have longer times of flight, and the process is known as "matrix-assisted laser desorption-ionization time-of-flight mass spectroscopy." MALDI-TOF-MS, as it is abbreviated, may be useful in analyzing STRs.

match. The presence of the same allele or alleles in two samples. Two DNA profiles are declared to match when they are indistinguishable in genetic type. For loci with discrete alleles, two samples match when they display the same set of alleles. For RFLP testing of VNTRs, two samples match when the pattern of the bands is similar and the positions of the corresponding bands at each locus fall within a preset distance. See match window, false match, true match.

match window. If two RFLP bands lie with a preset distance, called the match window, that reflects normal measurement error, they can be declared to match.

matter. All things of substance and is composed of atoms or molecules.

measurement scale. An object showing standard units of length (e.g., ruler) used in photographic documentation of an item of evidence.

medulla of a hair. A cellular column running through the center of the hair and having the appearance of a central canal running through it.

metabolize. Transforming a chemical in the body to another chemical for the purpose of facilitating its elimination from the body.

micro satellite. Another term for an STR.

microcrystalline test. Tests to identify specific substances by the color and morphology of the crystals formed when the substance is mixed with specific reagents.

minisatellite. Another term for a VNTR.

mitochondria. A structure (organelle) within nucleated (eukaryotic) cells that is the site of the energy producing reactions within the cell. Mitochondria contain their own DNA (often abbreviated as mtDNA), which is inherited only from mother to child.

molecular weight. The weight in grams of one mole of a pure, molecular substance.

monochromatic light. Light having a single wavelength or frequency.

monochromator. A device for isolating individual wavelengths or frequencies of light.

monomorphic. A gene or DNA characteristic that is almost always found in only one form in a population.

multilocus probe. A probe that marks multiple sites (loci). RFLP analysis using a multilocus probe will yield an autorad showing a striped pattern of thirty or more bands. Such probes rarely are used now in forensic applications in the United States.

multilocus profile. See profile.

multiple scenes. Two or more physical locations of evidence associated with a crime (e.g., in a crime of personal violence, evidence may be found at the location of the assault and also on the person and clothing of the victim/assailant, the victim's/assailant's vehicle, and locations the victim/assailant frequents and resides).

multiplexing. Typing several loci simultaneously.

mutation. The process that produces a gene or chromosome set differing from the type already in the population; the gene or chromosome set that results from such a process.

nanogram (ng). A billionth of a gram.

nonporous container. Packaging through which liquids or vapors cannot pass (e.g., glass jars or metal cans).

nuclear DNA. DNA present within the nucleus of a cell and this form is inherited from both parents.

nucleic acid. RNA or DNA.

nucleotide. A unit of DNA consisting of a base (A, C, G, or T) and attached to a phosphate and a sugar group; the basic building block of nucleic acids. See deoxyribonucleic acid.

nucleus. The membrane-covered portion of a eukaryotic cell containing most of the DNA and found within the cytoplasm.

oligo nucleotide. A synthetic polymer made up of fewer than 100 nucleotides; used as a primer or a probe in PCR. See primer.

oligospermia. A condition describing an abnormally low sperm count.

organic. A substance composed of carbon and hydrogen, and often, smaller amounts of oxygen, nitrogen, chlorine, phosphorus, or other elements i.e.. has a carbon base.

other responders. Individuals who are involved in an aspect of the crime scene, such as perimeter security, traffic control, media management, scene processing, and technical support, as well as prosecutors, medical personnel, medical examiners, coroners, forensic examiners, evidence technicians, and fire and rescue officers.

oxidation. A chemical reaction where oxygen is combined with other substances to produce new products. An example is iron in the presence of oxygen forms rust.

paternity index. A number (technically, a likelihood ratio) that indicates the support that the paternity test results lend to the hypothesis that the alleged father is the biological father as opposed to the hypothesis that another man selected at random is the biological father. Assuming that the observed phenotypes correctly represent the phenotypes of the mother, child, and alleged father tested, the number can be computed as the ratio of the probability of the phenotypes under the first hypothesis to the probability under the second hypothesis. Large values indicate substantial support for the hypothesis of paternity; values near zero indicate substantial support for the hypothesis that someone other than the alleged father is the biological father; and values near unity indicate that the results do not help in determining which hypothesis is correct.

personal protective equipment (PPE). Articles such as disposable gloves, masks, and eye protection that are utilized to provide a barrier to keep biological or chemical hazards from contacting the skin, eyes, and mucous membranes and to avoid contamination of the crime scene.

pH. A measure of the acidity of a solution.

phenotype. A trait, such as eye color or blood group, resulting from a genotype.

photomicrographs. Photo of a microscopic image.

photon. A small packet of electromagnetic radiation energy. Each photon contains a unit of energy equal to the product of Planck's constant and the frequency of radiation ($E=hf$).

polymarker. A commercially marketed set of PCR-based tests for protein polymorphisms.

polymer. A substance composed of a large number of atoms. These atoms are usually arranged in repeating units called monomers. DNA is an example of a polymer.

polymerase chain reaction (PCR). A process that mimics DNA's own replication processes to make up to millions of copies of short strands of genetic material in a few hours.

polymorphism. The presence of several forms of a gene or DNA characteristic in a population.

point mutation. See SNP.

population genetics. The study of the genetic composition of groups of individuals.

population structure. When a population is divided into subgroups that do not mix freely, that population is said to have structure. Significant structure can lead to allele frequencies being different in the subpopulations.

porous container. Packaging through which liquids or vapors may pass (e.g., paper bags, cloth bags).

presumptive test. A nonconfirmatory test used to screen for the presence of a substance.

primer. An oligonucleotide that attaches to one end of a DNA fragment and provides a point for more complementary nucleotides to attach and replicate the DNA strand. See oligonucleotide.

probe. In forensics, a short segment of DNA used to detect certain alleles. The probe hybridizes, or matches up, to a specific complementary sequence. Probes allow visualization of the hybridized DNA, either by radioactive tag (usually used for RFLP analysis) or biochemical tag (usually used for PCR-based analyses).

product rule. When alleles occur independently at each locus (Hardy-Weinberg equilibrium) and across loci (linkage equilibrium), the proportion of the population with a given genotype is the product of the proportion of each allele at each locus, times factors of two for heterozygous loci.

product rule. Multiplying together the frequencies of independently occurring genetic markers to obtain an overall frequency of occurrence for a genetic profile.

proficiency test. A test administered at a laboratory to evaluate its performance. In a blind proficiency study, the laboratory personnel do not know that they are being tested.

projectile trajectory analysis. The method for determining the path of a high-speed object through space (e.g., a bullet fired from a firearm).

prosecutor's fallacy. See transposition fallacy.

protein. A class of biologically important molecules made up of a linear string of building blocks called amino acids. The directions for the synthesis of any particular protein are encoded in the DNA sequence of its gene.

pyrolysis. The decomposition of organic matter by heat.

qualitative determination. Determination and identification of the combination of the components of a mixture.

quality assurance. A program conducted by a laboratory to ensure accuracy and reliability.

quality audit. A systematic and independent examination and evaluation of a laboratory's operations.

quality control. Activities used to monitor the ability of DNA typing to meet specified criteria.

quantitative determination. Determination of the actual amount of a specific compound in a mixture.

quinine. Bitter crystalline alkaloid from "cinchona bark" used in medicine to treat malaria. Along with talc is an additive to heroin to 'cut' the original concentration to street concentration.

radiological threat. The pending exposure to radiation energy. (This energy can be produced by shortwave x-rays or through unstable isotopes.)

random match. A match in the DNA profiles of two samples of DNA, where one is drawn at random from the population. See also random match probability.

random match probability. The chance of a random match. As it is usually used in court, the random match probability refers to the probability of a true match when the DNA being compared to the evidence DNA comes from a person drawn at random from the population. This random true match probability reveals the probability of a true match when the samples of DNA come from different, unrelated people.

random mating. The members of a population are said to mate randomly with respect to particular genes of DNA characteristics when the choice of mates is independent of the alleles.

reagent. A substance used, as in detecting or measuring a component, preparing a product, or developing a photograph because of the chemical or biological activity.

recombination. In general, any process in a diploid or partially diploid cell that generates new gene or chromosomal combinations not found in that cell or in its progenitors.

reference population. The population to which the perpetrator of a crime is thought to belong.

replication. The synthesis of new DNA from existing DNA. See polymerase chain reaction.

restriction enzyme. Protein that cuts double-stranded DNA at specific base pair sequences (different enzymes recognize different sequences). See restriction site.

restriction fragment length polymorphism (RFLP). Variation among people in the length of a segment of DNA cut at two restriction sites.

restriction fragment length polymorphism (RFLP) analysis. Analysis of individual variations in the lengths of DNA fragments produced by digesting sample DNA with a restriction enzyme.

restriction site. A sequence marking the location at which a restriction enzyme cuts DNA into fragments. See restriction enzyme.

Reverse Dot Blot. A detection method used to identify SNPs in which DNA probes are affixed to a membrane, and amplified DNA is passed over the probes to see if it contains the complementary sequence.

rigor mortis. Postmortem stiffening of the body in the position they are in when death occurs and usually assumes that of gravity. Begins immediately but not fully manifested until 6-8 hours in adults; begins to pass and the body becomes limp at about 24-36 hours. Rate of progression is environmentally dependent.

sequence-specific oligonucleotide (SSO) probe. See allele-specific oligonucleotide (ASO) probe.

sequencing. Determining the order of base pairs in a segment of DNA.

serology. Medical science dealing with blood serum and its reactions and properties.

short tandem repeat (STR). See variable number tandem repeat.

single-locus probe. A probe that only marks a specific site (locus). RFLP analysis using a single-locus probe will yield an autorad showing one band if the individual is homozygous, two bands if heterozygous.

single-use equipment. Items that will be used only once to collect evidence, such as biological samples, then discarded to minimize contamination (e.g., tweezers, scalpel blades, droppers).

smokeless powder. A type of gunpowder composed of a nitrocellulose compound and the current type used in bullets. Can be of two types: flake or ball.

SNP (single nucleotide polymorphism). A substitution, insertion, or deletion of a single base pair at a given point in the genome.

Southern blotting. Named for its inventor, a technique by which processed DNA fragments, separated by gel electrophoresis, are transferred onto a nylon membrane in preparation for the application of biological probes.

spectrophotometry. An analytical method for identifying a substance by its selective absorption of different wavelengths of light.

standard/reference sample. See comparison samples.

substrate controls. Uncontaminated surface areas collected at a crime scene near physical evidence to serve as a baseline to evaluate the retrieved evidence.

tandem repeats. A region of a chromosome that contains multiple copies of a core DNA sequences that are arranged in a repeating fashion.

team members. Individuals who are called to the scene to assist in investigation or processing of the scene (e.g., scientific personnel from the crime laboratory or medical examiner's office, other forensic specialists, photographers, mass disaster specialists, experts in the identification of human remains, arson and explosives investigators, clandestine drug laboratory investigators, as well as other experts).

telogen phase of hair growth. The final growth phase in which hair naturally falls out of the skin. Once hair growth ends, the telogen phase begins and the root takes on a club- shaped appearance.

tempered glass. Glass where strength is added by introducing stress through the rapid heating and cooling of the glass surfaces. When this type of glass is broken it shatters into small shards and can create patterned injuries.

tetrahydrocannabinol (THC). Chemical substance responsible for the hallucinogenic properties found in marijuana. Is the chemical property usually detected in a urine drug screen.

thymine (T). One of the four bases, or nucleotides, that make up the DNA double helix. Thymine only binds to adenine. See nucleotide.

trace evidence. Physical evidence that results from the transfer of small quantities of materials (e.g., hair, textile fibers, paint chips, glass fragments, gunshot residue particles).

transient evidence. Evidence which by its very nature or the conditions at the scene will lose its evidentiary value if not preserved and protected (e.g., blood in the rain).

transposition fallacy. Confusing the conditional probability of A given B [P(A |B)] with that of B given A [P(B | A)]. Few people think that the probability that a person speaks Spanish (A) given that he or she is a citizen of Chile (B) equals the probability that a person is a citizen of Chile (B) given that he or she speaks Spanish (A). Yet, many court opinions, newspaper articles, and even some expert witnesses speak of the probability of a matching DNA genotype (A) given that someone other than the defendant is the source of the crime scene DNA (B) as if it were the probability of someone else being the source (B) given the matching profile (A). Transposing conditional probabilities correctly requires Bayes' Theorem.

true match. Two samples of DNA that have the same profile should match when tested. If there is no error in the labeling, handling, and analysis of the samples and in the reporting of the results, a match is a true match. A true match establishes that the two samples of DNA have the same profile. Unless the profile is unique, however, a true match does not conclusively prove that the two samples came from the same source. Some people use "true match" more narrowly, to mean only those matches among samples from the same source. Compare false match. See also match, random match.

unknown/questioned. See comparison samples.

variable number tandem repeat (VNTR). A class of RFLPs due to multiple copies of virtually identical base pair sequences, arranged in succession at a specific locus on a chromosome. The number of repeats varies from individual to individual, thus providing a basis for individual recognition. VNTRs are longer than STRs.

walk-through. An initial assessment conducted by carefully walking through the scene to evaluate the situation, recognize potential evidence, and determine resources required. Also, a final survey conducted to ensure the scene has been effectively and completely processed.

window. See match window.

X chromosome. See chromosome.

Y chromosome. See chromosome.

Index